MAGIC SHADOWS

MAGIC SHADOWS

The Story of the Origin
of Motion Pictures

by

MARTIN QUIGLEY, JR.

GEORGETOWN UNIVERSITY PRESS

Washington, D. C.   1948

791.4

Qu 4 m

Copyright, 1948, by Martin Quigley, Jr.

24590

Oct '48

Set up in twelve point Garamond and printed by the
O'Brien Suburban Press, Inc., Norwalk, Connecticut

Printed in the United States of America

CONTENTS

ILLUSTRATIONS

FOREWORD

THIS VOLUME records first explorations of the path of light, ever widening from primitive dawn to the rainbow flood which now illuminates the world screen of the motion picture.

Here is a distillation from the adventures of a decade among the archives of Europe and America, many of them remote and never before examined in the perspective of today. This tracing of the long and often obscure way is not likely to be undertaken again for a century or two. It has been done *con amore,* but with a crisp objectivity, sharp precision. The work is a unique product of capacity, zeal and opportunity.

Primarily, this is the pre-history of the motion picture. Through it passes a pageant of philosophers, savants, priests, necromancers, tinkers, charlatans, scientists and entrepreneurs. Within its confines of the field of optics it is a cool study of human progress down the centuries.

In the lore of our Wild West is a tale of a woe bestricken, penniless prospector who stood hungrily watching a faro game. The sun flashed out as a cloud passed and through a knothole a spot of light, an image of the sun, fell on the layout. The hurrying, nonchalant dealer mistook it for a twenty dollar gold piece and paid off—whereby a fortune was founded. Something like that has given us the motion picture. This is the telling.

TERRY RAMSAYE

Tinker's Green
Wilton, Conn.
September 8, 1947

7

Ars Magna Lucis et Umbrae, 1671

ATHANASIUS KIRCHER, *the first person to project pictures. His magic lantern originated the screen art-science in Rome circa 1645.*

INTRODUCTION

THE ART of magic shadows, which just before the dawn of the twentieth century evolved into the modern motion picture, was born three centuries ago, at Rome. There Athanasius Kircher, a German priest, first showed his invention, the magic lantern, to friends, and enemies, at the Collegio Romano, where he was a professor of mathematics.

The world premiere of the first real "magic shadow" performance passed without public notice. In those days there were no press agents or publicists. There were no newspapers. The people did not care what the nobles and scholars were doing in their idle moments; the intellectuals paid little attention to the people.

History has not recorded the day and month in which Kircher presented his projector, the fundamental instrument of all screen shows, then and now. The occasion can be set only approximately —some time in the year 1644 or 1645. The hour of the performance presumably was in the evening, for the light and shadow pictures had to be shown in darkness, just as today films must be exhibited in darkened theatres.

We may be sure that the score or more of invited guests— Romans and distinguished foreigners—eagerly accepted an opportunity to see what Kircher was up to. Rome had been buzzing with rumors. The energetic little Jesuit priest who earned for himself the title, "Doctor of a Hundred Arts," had even been suspected of necromancy and working in league with the devil. After the showing of the magic lantern and its projected pictures some were certain that he practiced the "black arts."

The audience for the first screen performance was as distinguished as any that has since graced a Hollywood production. Other professors of the Roman College were there to note for themselves on which one of his "hundred arts" Kircher had been

9

busy. These men were among the most learned in Europe and had
made the Jesuit University, established in 1582, already an influence in all circles of thought. A selected group of students, young
Romans of noble birth, surely were also invited. Until the hour of
the demonstration, these stood outside in the large Piazza di Collegio Romano before the main entrance. Three centuries later,
from June, 1944 to late 1945, American Army MPs raced through
this same Piazza on jeeps and motorcycles to their headquarters in
Rome, just across the square from the entrance to the Collegio
Romano.

Just at the appointed hour for Kircher's show, a few distinguished monsignori, in flowing purple were driven to the entrance
in their carriages with mounted escort. Perhaps, too, a hush went
through the small group, assembled in an upper hall, when a
Prince of the Church, such as Cardinal Barberini who had summoned Kircher to Rome a decade before, came to see for himself.
After all the monsignori and other visitors had been greeted with
ceremony and salutation in keeping with their rank, the candles
and lamps were extinguished; Kircher slipped behind a curtain or
partition where his projector was concealed and the first light and
shadow screen show was on.

For a moment Kircher's audience could see nothing. Then
slowly their eyes became accustomed to the darkness and a faint
light appeared on a white surface set up in front of the few rows
of seats. As the flames in Kircher's lantern began to burn more
brightly and he adjusted the crude projection system, the picture
of his first glass slide was thrown upon the screen.

The young men with keen eyesight were the first to note that
the light and shadow on the screen, like some ghostly figment,
began to take form into a recognizable picture. Then the older
ecclesiastics saw or thought they saw. The incredulous murmured
prayerful ejaculations. The wonder increased as successive pictures
were projected. Kircher was enough of a showman to use pictures
which would entertain and amaze. He included animal drawings,
artistic designs and, to taunt those who thought he was dabbling
in necromancy, pictures of the devil. Prudence was not one of his
"hundred arts."

We may be amused now at the disbelief of Kircher's first audience. But by trying to place ourselves in that hall of the Roman
College, three centuries ago, it is easy to realize the difficulties.

Nothing like Kircher's show had ever been presented before. He had chained light and shadow, but the suspicion was held by some of the spectators that there was dark magic about it all and that Kircher had dabbled in the "black arts."

The first audience congratulated Kircher at the end of the performance, but some went away wondering, dubious. Years later, Kircher wrote in his autobiography, "New accusations piled up and my critics said I should devote my whole life to developing mathematics."

*

Two and a half centuries later, the screen art of magic shadow projection came to life in the motion picture. This was quite a different premiere. But Kircher would have recognized the device as an improvement on and development of his magic lantern. He, and hundreds who came after him, had tried to capture the animation of life in light and shadow pictures. Full success was not possible until a later date because the necessary materials were not available until near the end of the nineteenth century.

The scene of the most significant motion picture premiere was at Koster & Bial's Music Hall, 34th Street, New York, which stood on the site now occupied by the R. H. Macy department store. The time was April 23, 1896. But in contrast to Kircher's premiere, though "Thomas A. Edison's Latest Marvel—the Vitascope" had featured billing on the show, it was not the only entertainment on the program. Albert Bial, manager, preceded the showing of the motion pictures with a half-dozen acts of vaudeville. There were the Russian clown, eccentric dancer, athletic and gymnastic comedian, singers and actors and actresses. But the movies stole that show and, in little more than a decade, became staple entertainment in tens of thousands of theatres all over the world.

The special top hat and silk tie audience at Koster & Bial's Music Hall that Spring evening a half-century ago was treated to a selection of short films which ran only a few moments each: "Sea Waves", "Umbrella Dance", "The Barber Shop", "Burlesque Boxing", "Monroe Doctrine", "A Boxing Bout", "Venice, Showing Gondolas", "Kaiser Wilhelm, Reviewing His Troops", "Skirt Dance", "Butterfly Dance", "The Bar Room" and "Cuba Libre".

Thomas Armat, the inventor of the projector which had been built by Edison, supervised projection of those first screen motion pictures shown on Broadway. We can well imagine that Kircher was looking over his shoulder, delighted that his work started 250 years before had been brought to the triumph of the living moving picture.

The great Edison was in a box at the Music Hall that evening and he, too, was glad that the New York audience of first nighters so well received the large screen motion pictures. A few years before, his Kinetograph camera and his Kinetoscope peep-hole viewer had presented motion pictures. But as Kircher in the 17th century wanted his pictures life-size on the screen, so did the public of the Nineties.

*

Kircher and Edison do not stand alone in the parade of pioneers in the art and science of the screen. The list of builders of the cinema is as cosmopolitan as its appeal: Greeks, Romans, Persians, British, Italians, Germans, French, Belgians, Austrians and lastly, and in some ways most importantly, Americans. Ancient philosophers, medieval monks, scholarly giants of the Renaissance, scientists, necromancers, modern inventors—all had a role in the 2500 year story of the creation, out of light and shadow, of this most popular and most influential expression—the motion picture.

Great and strange men, some whose fame derives from activities in other fields, others hardly recorded in the passing of history, contributed to what was eventually to become the motion picture. Many of the pioneers of the magic shadow art-science realized the entertainment, educational and scientific potentialities of their discoveries; others did not, because they were preoccupied with other affairs and only toyed with the light and shadow devices.

The following chapters tell how men learned about vision and light, and how apparatus to record and project living realities was developed.

It is the story of the origin of the motion picture, from Adam to Edison.

IT STARTED WITH "A"

~ First magic shadow show—Ancient optical studies—Chinese Shadow Plays, Japanese and English mirrors—The art-science begins with Aristotle and Archimedes, Greeks, and Alhazen, an Arab.

FROM ANY VIEWPOINT the story of the origin of the motion picture begins with "A". The fundamental and instinctive urge to create pictures in living reality goes all the way back to Adam. Aristotle developed the theoretical basis of the science of optics. Archimedes made the first systematic use of lenses and mirrors. Alhazen, the Arab, pioneered in the study of the human eye, a prerequisite for developing machines to duplicate requisite functions of the human eye.

Lights and shadows were made when the night and the day were made:

And God said: Be light made. And light was made.
And God saw the light that it was good; and He
divided the light from the darkness.
And He called the light Day, and the darkness Night;
and there was evening and morning one day.

. . . .

And God said: Let there be lights made in the
firmament of heaven . . .
And God made two great lights: a greater light to
rule the day; and a lesser light to rule the night;
and the stars.   —*Book of Genesis*

The moon playing upon silent waters, the sun casting deepening shadows in the woods, a twinkling campfire, starlight dancing on ruffled waters—all provided the first pageantries of light and shadow. The first eclipse of the sun seen by man was the most thrilling and terrifying light and shadow show of that era, a premiere never rivalled by Hollywood's best.

From the beginning of the record of human aspiration men had the urge to create representations of life. Efforts were made to duplicate in permanent form the pictures reflected in still water, shadows, and birds and animals and people. And so, in a very early day man took up drawing, a variation of light and shadow portrayal. But the early drawings, and attempts for centuries thereafter, did not wholly succeed in their purpose. Life of the surrounding world could not be caught in all its wondrous detail no matter how skilled was the artist. The first picture critics pointed out that the drawings were unnatural because no action was shown and life itself was full of motion.

For cinema purposes, one of the earliest examples of "motion" still pictures is a representation of a boar trotting along, for some 10,000, 20,000 or 30,000 years, on a wall of the Font-de-Faune cave at Altamira near Santillana del Mar in Northern Spain. The artist tried to show the boar's headlong pace by equipping the animal with two complete sets of legs. It was recognized a long while before Walt Disney that more than one still picture was necessary to portray natural motion.

For centuries artists continued to strive for the "illusion" of motion without "moving pictures." Depending on the skill of the artist, the result approached the goal in varying degrees. Action was always, and still is, a problem to the artist working with a "still" medium. A pinnacle of success in this quest was reached in the Winged Victory of Samothrace in which the artist did all in his power to show motion in the medium of cold, lifeless marble.

However, the potential progress was limited as long as it was necessary to rely upon the skilled hand of the artist to convey motion. More had to be learned about light and shadow and also a great deal about the everlasting wonder of the human eye before living reality could be captured for future representation.

The poets may speculate about man's first thoughts on light, the sun, moon and stars, and fire. But man used his eyes for ages before he became interested and considered why and how he could see, and what light and shadow might be and how they could be usefully harnessed. Even in our day of apparent enlightenment, the underlying explanation of vision and light still eludes our scientists, so we should be patient about the time it took our ancestors to devise ways of harnessing light and shadow to prepare the brightly lighted way for the Bing Crosbys and Betty Grables of our day.

The study of light and vision, and the need for better methods and instruments for observing life resulted in time in the invention of the first optical device—the magnifying glass. All telescopes, microscopes, spectacles, cameras, projectors and other optical instruments have been evolved from the simple lens or magnifying glass. That lens was a special boon to the men and women who through birth, age or misfortune had poor eyesight.

Some authorities hold that as long ago as 6000 B.C. magnifying glasses were used by the Chaldeans in the ancient biblical lands. It is known that the Chaldeans, who developed an elaborate civilization, gave first attention to the study of light and all its problems. A few thousand years before the new era the Babylonians, famed too as gardeners, became great astronomers. The heavens, then and now, present the greatest natural light and shadow show, with a continuous run every night since the beginning of time. So it is not surprising that the first study of light and shadow should concern itself with the stars and planets. The Babylonians, with but the naked eye, picked out constellations and identified them. It was a desire to learn more about the stars that resulted in the development of a telescope, which was a marked advance in the science of light and shadow.

In the ruins of Nineveh, destroyed in 606 B.C., was found a convex lens of quartz and an inscription too fine to be read by the naked eye—proof that those people knew the uses of lenses and treasured fine artistic drawings and writings which could be inscribed only through the use of a magnifying glass.

*

At an early date the conflict arose between those who wished to use the magic shadows to entertain and instruct and those who wished to use them for purposes of deception.

The Egyptian priests have first claim on the title of light and shadow showmen. Some of the fragments of hieroglyphics indicate that they used optical devices to deceive. It is likely that a simple mirror was used to throw images into space. But that would have amazed the people and would have been taken as a sure sign of miraculous power.

The oldest media of light and shadow entertainment and deception was developed by another great and scholarly group, the early Chinese scientists. These were the Chinese Shadow Plays, the origin of which is lost in antiquity, dating back perhaps to 5000 B. C. Silhouette figures shown on a background of smoke and animated as in a puppet show entertained a public thousands of years ago in the Far East. The Chinese Shadow Plays appear to have a close relation to the old-time fireside tricks of twisting the fingers so as to form what appeared to be the shadow of a donkey's head or a representation of a rabbit or of some other animal. Despite the troubled history of China, these Shadow Plays were never lost and they are still presented in remote parts of China and in Java.

Dates of the Chinese contributions to the story of the origin of the cinema and related sciences are uncertain. The Chinese empire was founded around 2800 B.C. and within 500 years of that time the heavens had been charted by the Chinese. A hundred years after an hereditary monarchy was established in China, about 2200 B.C., the ruling powers executed two astronomers for failing to observe properly an eclipse of the sun.

After the Chinese Shadow Plays, mention should be made of another Oriental light and shadow invention. This one was developed by the Japanese. The devices are known as Japanese Mirrors. These are famed in legend and history as being endowed with great magical powers. They, as in the inventions of the Egyptians, used an optical illusion to entertain and also to trick.

The method of the Japanese Mirrors was simple: They were of polished bronze with a design embossed on the surface. When held to the sun, the reflected light would fall on a wall or other smooth surface, and the spectators would see the design, appearing as if through the power of the devil or some propitious deity. If the operator did not allow his mirror to be closely examined by the audience he could certainly be credited with magical powers—the power to bring animals and men, and any kind of design to life. Not a devil or a god; but in reality only an early showman! And done with mirrors!

The so-called English Mirrors, of a much later date, worked on a similar principle, but were even more ingenious. They had greater "magical" power. The English Mirrors resembled the Japanese Mirrors, yet on close examination no embossing would be discovered on the surface. Even today one might have a difficult time discovering the secret.

The picture to be projected was very carefully and lightly etched with acid upon the brass surface of the English Mirrors. The mirror was then polished until the etched pattern could not be detected by eye or touch. But the imperceptible roughness outlining the pattern remained on the mirror and was sufficient to record and reflect the outline of the design in what seemed a magical fashion.

After a vague start in Babylonia, Egypt and the Far East, the study of light and shadow, like many another art and science, began in a thorough way in Greece.

Aristotle, great Greek philosopher, born about 384 B.C., made the first important contribution to the history of the light and shadow art-science which can be assigned to an identifiable individual.

Aristotle's family had been long identified with medicine. His father was court physician to the King of Macedonia and several of his ancestors had similar posts. Therefore, in a sense, it was natural for him to seek learning. For some years he was a student of the philosopher Plato at Athens. He was a more practical man than his teacher, favoring experimental observation as supplemental to philosophy.

Universal truth and knowledge were the goals Aristotle set for himself. Also he believed it well to keep in the good graces of the rulers. When Alexander the Great was 13 years old, Aristotle was appointed his teacher and from that time on had a deep influence on the pupil who, they tell us, came to tears because he had no more worlds to conquer. Aristotle later headed the Peripatetic or "walk about" school at Athens, so named because knowledge was imparted from teacher to student as they strolled about the groves. Aristotle wrote authoritatively on almost every subject. The sun, light, and vision, of course, received the attention of this philosopher whose word on philosophic and scientific matters was accepted by many without question as law for centuries. Even today many principles first enunciated by Aristotle are still generally respected in philosophy.

In Aristotle's book titled *Problems* there was described the phenomenon of sunlight passing through a square hole and still casting an image of a round—not square—sun on the wall or floor.

This was an astounding discovery! It may strike the reader as strange, but he may easily convince himself by making a little experiment: cut a square hole in a piece of dark paper and let the image of the sun fall on a mirror or other smooth surface and you will see that the sun is still round despite the square hole. As a word of caution, one must be careful to avoid eye strain when viewing the sun and its reflections. Several of the principal characters in motion picture pre-history ruined their eyes by studying the sun for too long a period at one time.

Aristotle's square hole and round sun experiment was a beginning and scientists were starting to learn something important about light and optical phenomena.

Aristotle also made a valuable contribution to the study of vision. In his book, *On Dreams,* he noted the existence of afterimages, a persistence of vision phenomenon. That faculty contributes vitally to the motion picture effect. A common example is that a whirling firebrand appears to make a complete continuous circle of fire. A strong light or image of any kind will be visible to the eye for a moment after the physical stimulus has been removed.

Aristotle also was interested in color and in a study in this connection he noted that certain given plants were bleached by the sun. This was the initial scientific observation in the chain which ultimately, though indirectly, led to photography.

Archimedes (287-212 B.C.), a half-century after Aristotle, developed at Syracuse, then a Greek colony on the island of Sicily, the first recorded light apparatus, "The Burning Mirrors or Lenses." Famed as the first great geometrician, Archimedes is best known for his principle upon which all ship construction is based—the buoyant force exerted by a liquid is equal to the weight of the displaced liquid. In other words, a shaped object of metal, such as a ship, will float if it displaces a sufficient quantity of water. King Hiero of Syracuse, a relative of Archimedes, gave him the problem of determining whether or not a new crown he had received was made of pure gold, as ordered, or whether the gold had been mixed with silver. This would have been no task at all if the King had not been fond of the crown and wished the information secured without damaging it in any way. As was the custom in those days, Archimedes considered the problem one afternoon at the local bath which served the double function of promoting cleanliness and of fostering every kind of discussion. It was the gentlemen's club of the day and place.

Archimedes liked to bathe with a tub full of water and this particular afternoon he noted that a considerable amount of water was spilled over the sides of the tub as he stepped in. He immediately and correctly concluded that there was a relation between the mass of his body and the weight of the water displaced. Then according to tradition he rushed home, through the streets of Syracuse, naked, in order to test the King's crown, shouting "Eureka—I have found it."

This talented Greek was keenly aware of his scientific prowess and was not a man to keep his ideas secret. He promised to lift the world with a lever (the principle of which he had developed scientifically) provided someone would furnish him a fulcrum. There were no takers.

When Archimedes was 73 years old and respected throughout the civilized world for his work in mathematics and science, the Roman invader Marcellus lay siege to Syracuse. At the beginning of the two long years of struggle, Archimedes put aside his theoretical work and with the vigor of a youth helped to defend the city, inventing numerous engines of war for the purpose. In this he was the real pioneer of the scientists of our own day who perfected in wartime the atomic bomb, radar and other devices.

Archimedes' most important development in his martial pursuits was the Great Burning Glasses or Lenses upon which much of his fame has since rested. According to tradition, the Great Burning Glasses of Archimedes were used to burn the fleets of Marcellus, acting on the same principle used by the modern Boy Scout or woodsman in starting a fire with a pocket magnifying glass.

The efficacy of Archimedes' lenses for burning purposes has been argued for centuries. This much is certain: they did not succeed in their purpose for Marcellus sacked the city in 212 B.C., after the walls had been stormed. Archimedes was killed but after his death he was honored even by the invader Marcellus, who ordered a monument erected over his grave.

One explanation is that the Burning Glasses of Archimedes were used in what would now be called psychological warfare. Archimedes knew how to construct glasses, systems that would set small fires at a close range; the enemy knew this. So what better ruse would there be than to construct a gigantic Burning Glass atop the highest building of Syracuse, clearly in view of the enemy fleet and let the intelligence report leak out that on such and such a day Archimedes was going to burn up the whole fleet and raise the siege? One can imagine what the effect was on the sailors and officers of the fleet, including Marcellus himself. Archimedes' strategy might have prolonged the defense through a great part of the two years in which the city resisted. The main problem, of course, and suspicion in the minds of the enemy was—could Archimedes actually burn the fleet with his mysterious mirrors and lenses? (Illustration facing page 32.)

The possibility of actual use of the Burning Glasses to start fires on the ships of an invader was not entirely dismissed by Athanasius Kircher who made a special trip to Syracuse in 1636 to study the problem on the spot. He wrote in the same book in which the magic lantern is described that he had constructed a burning glass or lens which started a fire at a distance of 12 feet and that a friend of his, Manfred Septal, on February 15, 1645, shortly before Kircher's book was completed, had started a fire at 15 paces.

Kircher did not believe burning glasses could be used to start a fire at a great distance as claimed by some scientists and experimenters. He said that Cardano's story of burning at 1,000 paces was ridiculous, as were exaggerated claims of Porta. But Kircher did point out that there may be something of truth in the original story of Archimedes because, in his opinion, ships of the attacking force would be anchored just off the walls of the city, perhaps only 25 to 50 feet away. This was done so the full force of the fleet's armament of the day could be thrown against the defenders on the walls and yet the men of the ships would be out of range of hand-to-hand encounters with the Syracusans.

Kircher reasoned that a great Burning Glass could start a fire in a ship right under the walls of the city if the glass were mounted on top of a nearby building. It is likely that at the most Archimedes would have been able to start only a small fire on the sail of one of the enemy's ships.

Archimedes' Burning Glasses are the only real ancient optical instruments about which we have a contemporary or nearly contemporary record. These early water-filled glasses were the first projection lenses. Archimedes' Burning Glasses played an important part in the developments which led to the modern motion picture because, without lenses for the projection, films would be nothing but peep-shows, visible to one person at a time. Without lenses our cameras would be very crude instruments. In a true sense the focused mirror or lens burning glass is the foundation of every kind of camera and all projection work.

Aristotle and Archimedes and other Greek scientists, including Euclid, who is credited with being the first to demonstrate that light travels in straight lines, opened the book of knowledge of the light and shadow art.

Ptolemy who flourished at Alexandria around 130 A.D. was the greatest scientist of his era and his influence was powerful for fifteen centuries. It was he who developed the Ptolemaic theory which viewed the earth as the center of the universe, with the sun and other bodies revolving around it. That theory very naturally tended to increase man's idea of his own importance. Ptolemy was a geographer and mathematician as well as an astronomer. His great work was called *Almagest* by the Arabs. Ptolemy discussed the persistence of vision, the laws of reflection and made studies of refraction.

The poor tools then available and inaccurate understanding of some basic principles prevented in ancient days the discovery of devices capable of capturing the illusion of motion. History played its part, too.

After the stimulus given to all knowledge by the Greeks, little interest in the arts and sciences was taken anywhere for a long time. Then in the 9th century the scholarship of Greece was advanced by the Arabs, from whom Europe began to receive it in the 12th century. During the early Middle Ages, the real "Dark Ages" when barbarian hordes overran much of Europe, the seat of learning was in the Near East, in Arabia and Persia.

Today it may be difficult for some to attribute great intellectual advance to a people often associated in the common mind with desert life and the crudities of camel transport. But around the year 850 A.D. the most elaborate courts of the world, and keenest scholarship, were in the Near East. The latest of the ancient pioneers in magic shadows, the fourth "A", was Alhazen, the Arab.

Alhazen (Abu Ali Alhasan Ibn Alhasan, Ibnu-l-Haitam or Ibn Al-Haitan) was the greatest Arab scientist in the field of optics and vision. Born in 965 at Basra, Arabian center of commerce and learning, near the Persian Gulf, Alhazen from an early age devoted himself to science of a practical rather than theoretical nature. He was what would be called a civil engineer in our day.

At the invitation of the King of Egypt, Alhazen undertook the gigantic task of regulating the Nile. He was indeed a man of courage. Even back in those days the floods of that great river were a serious menace to lives and property, and control was attempted. But it was not until modern times that any successful regulation of the flood waters of the Nile was effected, and this was under the skill of British engineering; so Alhazen should not be blamed for his failure.

Alhazen went to Egypt and made preliminary calculations. He saw that the task was impossible with available tools, men and knowledge, but to admit failure in those days usually meant losing a life—one's own. Absolute rulers did not like to have agreements broken. Alhazen feigned madness and escaped. By pretending to lose his head he saved his life.

Despite his failure with the Nile, Alhazen is regarded as the first great discoverer in optics after the time of Ptolemy. The Arabs were enthusiastic followers of Aristotle and also knew of the work of Archimedes, Ptolemy and other Greek scholars.

Alhazen's great work, *Opticae Thesaurus Alhazeni Arabis,* was first printed in 1572 but manuscript copies of the *De Aspectibus* or *Perspectiva* and the *De Crepusculis & Nubium Ascensionibus* had found their way about the late 12th century into all the great libraries of the Middle Ages and his influence on all subsequent work in optics was great and widespread. The book is very curious, covering a multitude of subjects. Alhazen studied images, the various kinds of shadows and even attempted to calculate the size of the earth. He is credited with being the first to explain successfully the apparent increase of heavenly bodies near the horizon—the familiar phenomenon of the great sun at sunset and the huge harvest moon as it comes up in the East. Light also was extensively considered by Alhazen and he treated its use, setting down many rules on reflection and refraction. He recognized the element of time necessary to complete the act of vision; in other words, the persistence of vision or the time lag. He gave a description of the lens' magnifying power as he was familiar with various lenses and mirrors.

But, perhaps of most importance, Alhazen was the first to note in some detail the workings of the human eye. Alhazen discussed how we see but one picture even though we have two eyes, both functioning at the same time. He is also one of the authorities who made it possible for later scholars to know that the Greeks and Phoenicians knew and understood the simpler optical phenomena.

It would be expecting too much to hope that Alhazen's work would be unmixed with error. At his time and for centuries later, on account of the lack of suitable instruments and knowledge of what was being sought, the imagination was relied on more than it should have been in an exact science.

In early days much of the advance in learning had to be reasoned out and then verified, if possible, by experiments. Now we reverse the process. Our scientists experiment first by observing phenomena under all sorts of conditions and then later try to reason to a satisfactory explanation which, even with all our learning, cannot always be found. In fact, the underlying explanation of many of the commonest things in life escape us. For example, we do not know a great deal more than the ancients about the ultimate constituents of matter, the nature of light or how our senses really work.

Alhazen did valuable work himself but was far more important as the inspiration for study in optics for the greatest scientist of the Middle Ages, the first experimental scientist and one of the greatest Englishmen of all time, Roger Bacon.

II

FRIAR BACON'S MAGIC

*꒝ Roger Bacon, English monk of the
13th Century, studies the ancients—and
the Greeks—and inaugurates the scientific study of magic shadows and devices
for creating them.*

ROGER BACON made a great contribution to human knowledge,
especially in scientific matters. Yet this great philosopher
and scientist was generally regarded as "Friar Bacon," a mad
monk who played with magic and dealt with the powers of darkness. This myth persisted even though Bacon's contemporaries
had bestowed upon him the title of "Doctor Mirabilis." Studies
made in the 19th century and the first part of this century have
tended to confirm him in his proper high place in history.

Roger Bacon was born at Ilchester in Somersetshire, England,
about 1214, the year before the Magna Charta was signed. In
those days serious education began early. When Bacon was 12
or 13 he was sent to Oxford. Later on he continued his studies at
Paris. In his youth Bacon's family gave him the considerable
sums he needed for his education.

After completing his studies, Bacon was a professor at Oxford
and then entered the Franciscan Order. As a monk he found
the pursuit of learning somewhat more difficult even though the
libraries of the religious orders were the best of the period and
most of the learned men were ecclesiastics. After having taken
a vow of poverty Bacon had difficulty in obtaining from some
of his superiors money to buy pens and pay copyists. Certain
authorities did not look with complete satisfaction on his experi-

24

mental science investigations and they liked even less his barbed comments on other philosophers of the day.

Bacon as a member of the Franciscan Order found himself confronted with the rule requiring his superiors' permission to publish any work. However, Pope Clement IV, a Frenchman, had the requirement lifted so far as Bacon was concerned by personally communicating with him and asking him to publish his studies. When that Pope was Cardinal Guy le Gros de Foulques (or Foulquois), the Papal Delegate in England, he had been impressed with Bacon's scholarship.

Following the Pope's command, Bacon set out to do the job. After some difficulty in obtaining money for pens and copyists, the three great works, *Opus Majus, Minus* and *Tertium* (1267-68) were completed in the almost unbelievable time of 18 months. These, together with his short book, "Concerning the marvelous power of art and nature and the ineffectiveness of magic"—also known as "Letter concerning the secret works of art and nature" —are his best known writings.

As soon as his first book was completed Bacon sent it off to the Pope in care of his friend, John of Paris. Unfortunately, Pope Clement IV died within a year of receiving Bacon's book and no official papal action was taken in connection with his scientific opinions. Bacon continued to teach, study and experiment at Oxford where he held for a time the office of Chancellor. Some say he was eventually imprisoned; the record is not clear.

The most interesting part of Bacon's work, so far as motion picture prehistory is concerned, is contained in his letter "On the Power of Art and Nature and Magic." It is in this work that Bacon speaks of the many wonderful devices he knows about and which would be in service in the future. Here we read of self-propelled vehicles, under-water craft, flying machines, gun-powder (the idea of which probably came from the East), lenses, microscopes, telescopes. Bacon claimed that he had seen all these wonderful things with the exception of the flying machine. But even this did not leave him at a loss, for he tells us that he has seen drawings by a man who has it all worked out on paper!

In that book of Bacon there is also the theory of going westward to India—the idea that later resulted in the discovery of America. The idea, therefore, was not original with Christopher Columbus. Bacon deserves great credit, for his views at least had a direct influence. His statements were used without credit by Pierre d'Ailly in his *Imago Mundi,* published in 1480. We know Columbus consulted this work, for he quoted a passage in his letter to Ferdinand and Isabella when seeking financial support for the voyage. And it was the very passage of Bacon, stolen by d'Ailly, which Columbus used to drive home his arguments with the King and Queen of Spain.

Bacon devoted ten whole years to the study of optics and some of his best work was done in that field. The principal influence on Bacon in this subject was the work of Alhazen, the Arab. The concentration of rays and the principal focus, knowledge necessary for fine camera work, as well as good picture projection, were familiar to Bacon. This was an advance over Euclid, Ptolemy and Alhazen. Bacon recognized that light had a measurable speed. Up to that time most men thought that the speed of light was infinite. (Measurements were not made until the 19th century.) Bacon also studied the optical illusions pertaining to motion and rest, fundamental for the motion picture. He belonged to the school of vision study that believed we see by something shot out from the objects viewed. This is directly opposed to the idea of Lucretius and others who held that something was shot out of the eye to make sight possible. There is no evidence that Bacon actually invented a telescope but he certainly was aware of the principle. He planned a combination of lenses which would bring far things near.

Roger Bacon has often been called the inventor of the *camera obscura,* or "dark room," which is the heart of the system for taking and exhibiting pictures. (Illustration facing page 40.)

However, the original of the modern box pin-hole camera in its simplest form is only a dark room with a very small hole in one wall, and was never actually invented. The phenomenon of an image of what was on the outside appearing upside down in a dark room was surely a natural discovery first observed in the remote past. The "dark room" can easily be considered as a giant box camera with the spectator inside the box. An inverted image of the scene outside appears on the wall or floor with the light coming through a small circular opening, as in a "pin-hole" camera.

Record of the first use of the "dark room" for entertainment or science has been lost in the dim past. As late as 1727 the

French *Dictionnaire Universel* suggested, in desperation, that Solomon himself must have invented the room camera. Until the 13th century, the images in the room camera were faint and upside down because no lens system was used. In ancient days and through the Middle Ages the camera was a wonderful and terrifying thing. The theatre always was some small darkened room. With a brilliant sun and the necessary small hole and a white wall or floor, the outside scene would be projected. Spectators and students certainly were thrilled and awed.

The Romans learned about the camera from the Greeks, who probably had obtained the knowledge from the East where, with brilliant sun in which the best results could be obtained, it is likely the effects were first noticed. Such learned Arabs as Alhazen are believed to have had a knowledge of the use of the room camera, but Alhazen did not leave any good description of it in his writings.

To Bacon must go the credit for the first description of the camera used for scientific purposes. Two Latin manuscripts, attributed to him or one of his pupils, in which the use of the room camera to observe an eclipse is described, have been found in the French National Library. It was pointed out that this method makes it possible for the astronomer to observe the eclipse without endangering his eyesight by staring at the sun.

It is certain Bacon used a mirror-lens device for entertainment and instruction. In his *Perspectiva* there appears the following passage:

> Mirrors can be so arranged that, as often as we wish, any object, either in the house or the street, can be made to appear. Anyone looking at the images formed by the mirrors will see something real but when he goes to the place where the object seems to be he will find nothing. For the mirrors are so cleverly arranged in relation to the object that the images appear to be in space, formed there by the union of the visible rays. And the spectators will run to the place of the apparitions where they think the objects actually are, but will find nothing but an illusion of the object.

Bacon's description is not clear: the effects and not the apparatus are described. The words could apply to a variation of the camera principle but it seems more likely that only a mirror system, related to the modern periscope, was used. The device did not achieve projection in the strict sense. Bacon's description clearly states that through the use of mirrors objects were made to appear where they were not. In effect, this reminds us of the illusion of the modern motion picture. There are stories that native people when first seeing motion pictures, attempt to run up to the screen and greet the pictures. It is only through experience that they learn the characters are not actually alive on the screen.

Bacon knew that light and shadow instruments were not always used for worthy purposes of entertainment or instruction but were also used to deceive. He vigorously attacked the practices of necromancy—showing the correctness of his position even though in gossip his name has been linked with the "Black Art", as was Kircher's four centuries later.

"For there are persons," Bacon wrote, "who by a swift movement of their limbs or a changing of their voice or by fine instruments or darkness or the cooperation of others produce apparitions, and thus place before mortals marvels which have not the truth of actual existence." Bacon added that the world was full of such fakers. It is not surprising that those skilled in the black arts tried to use the strange medium of light and shadow to impose upon the ignorant and unwary.

The death of Roger Bacon in 1294 was the passing of one of the greatest men in the history of light and shadow. With him the art-science had reached a point at which magic shadow entertainment devices could be built. Friar Bacon did much more to prepare the way for devices which were not to be perfected for centuries than merely make a contribution to the knowledge of light, lenses and mirrors. He blazed the way for all later experimental scientists. Up to his time emphasis had been placed on theoretical, speculative thinking. Bacon showed that science must be based on practical experimentation as the foundation for its principles.

III

DA VINCI'S CAMERA

❧ Italy of the Renaissance dominates magic shadow development—Leonardo da Vinci describes in detail the camera obscura — Inventions are by Alberti, Maurolico, Cesariano and Cardano.

To THE GIANT of the Renaissance, Leonardo da Vinci, must go the credit for being the first to determine and record the principles of the *camera obscura,* or "dark room", basic instrument of all photography. Da Vinci lived in a wondrous age. Michelangelo was painting and sculpturing his unparalleled creations. Raphael was at work. The Italians of the Renaissance led the world in a new culture. The torch of learning and art once held high in Greece, then at ancient Rome, later by the Arabs, was carried high in Italy of the late Middle Ages.

Together with the general Renaissance in Italy there was a rebirth of interest in optics and especially light and shadow demonstrations and devices. The new activity had come after a second "dark age" of nearly two centuries, from the time of Roger Bacon to da Vinci. After this "dark age" the room box-camera was "rediscovered" in Italy. Of course, as noted above, since the camera had never been invented in the usual sense of the term, it was not actually "rediscovered" either. It is likely that da Vinci and others received their stimulus in this general subject from Bacon and perhaps Alhazen or Witelo.

The renewed interest in scenic beauty in the Renaissance suggested work with a portable camera, as it was found to be an excellent aid in painting and drawing the beauties of nature.

29

Leone Battista Alberti (1404-1472), a Florentine ecclesiastic and artist, was the first Italian to make a notable contribution to the magic shadow story. Alberti, like the greater da Vinci, had many talents. A native of Florence, he grew up in an atmosphere of artistic culture. He was a priest, poet, musician, painter and sculptor, but most noted as an architect. He wrote *De Re Aedificatoria,* "Concerning architecture or building", published after his death in 1485 and many other works, including *Della Famiglia,* "The Family".

Alberti completed work on the Pitti Palace in Florence but his best design is said to be the St. Francis Church at Rimini. He also designed the new facade of St. Maria Novella Church at Florence and is believed to be the architect of the unfinished courtyard at the Palazzo Venezia which nearly 500 years later was the office of the late and unlamented Benito Mussolini. His painting, "La Visitazione", is in the Uffizi gallery. As an ecclesiastic, Alberti was Canon of the Metropolitan Church of Florence in 1447 and later was Abbot of the San Sovino monastery, Pisa.

But it was as an artist that Alberti made his contribution to the art and science of light and shadows. He invented the *camera lucida,* a machine which aided artists and painters by reflecting images and scenes to be painted or drawn. The device, a modification of the "dark room", could also be used to make it easy to copy a design. In a sense, the *camera lucida* was the forerunner of the modern blue-print duplicator. After Alberti had made his original drawings, an assistant, with the aid of the device, could rapidly copy them and give duplicates to the builders for use on the construction job.

Vasari's *Lives of Painters, Sculptors and Architects* is the chief source of information about Alberti. That writer said Alberti was more anxious for invention than for fame and had more interest in experimenting than in publishing his results. This is an attempt to explain why Alberti's own words of description of his *camera lucida* are not preserved.

Alberti was said to have written on the art of representation, explaining his "depictive showings" which "spectators found unbelievable". According to Vasari's description it would appear that Alberti used a form of the *camera obscura* or room box-camera but introduced special scenes such as paintings of mountains and the seas and the stars. In this way Alberti sought to introduce a

touch of showmanship into the performances of the room camera
which up to this time was used chiefly for observation of eclipses
and other scientific purposes.

Though Alberti died when Leonardo da Vinci was a young
man, it is certain that Leonardo knew of him, as they were natives
of the same city. Perhaps da Vinci had even attended some of
Alberti's magic shadows exhibitions.

Leonardo di Ser Piero da Vinci was born near Florence in
1452 and died near Amboise, France, in 1519. In 1939, 420
years after his death, a great exhibition of the master's works
was held at Milan and parts of it were shown in the next year at
the Museum of Science and Industry in Rockefeller Center, New
York. The Milan exhibit included works in the following fields:
studies and drawings in mathematics, astronomy, geology, geodesy,
cosmography, map-making, hydraulics, botany, anatomy, optics
(including proof of Alhazen's problem of measuring the angle
of reflection of light), acoustics, mechanics, and flying; not to
mention sculpture, painting, drawing, sketches, architecture, town
planning and military arts and sciences.

Da Vinci is best known today for his paintings, such as the
renowned "Last Supper", beloved everywhere, and the "Mona
Lisa". He was one of the truly universal geniuses. There was little
indeed that he could not do.

Leonardo's study of optics and perspective was reported in his
Treatise on Painting, written about 1515 and first published at
Paris in 1651, but well known prior to that time through manuscript copies. Da Vinci has been a great trial to the students and
historians, for he wrote in his own special form of shorthand
which was found to be extremely hard to decipher.

Da Vinci experimented with the *camera obscura* and wrote an
accurate scientific description of it, preparing the way for the
men who were to make the machine a practical medium. Vasari
in his famous *Life of Leonardo* points out that he gave his attention
to mirrors and learned how they operated and how images were
formed. But more important than this, he studied the human
eye and was the first to explain it accurately, using the camera
as his model, and in this way he really learned the fundamentals
of its functional principles. To this day the camera is explained
in simplest terms as a mechanical eye and the human eye is
explained as a marvelous, natural camera. Da Vinci also noted

the effects of visible impressions on the eye.

Roger Bacon was undoubtedly Leonardo's master in optics and this is a definite link in the chain of the growing knowledge of light and shadow and of devices which would create illusions for instruction and entertainment. It has been pointed out that Leonardo and Roger Bacon had much in common—both being so far ahead of their own times that they were not understood until centuries later. And both men believed passionately in scientific research and investigation. As an example, Leonardo would spend hours, days or even weeks studying a muscle of an animal appearing in the background of a painting so that it could be drawn perfectly. As a concrete link with Bacon, Leonardo described a mirror camera device which made it possible for people on the inside to see the passerby in the street outside. Bacon, you may recall, achieved and described a similar effect.

Within two years after da Vinci's death two other Italians, Maurolico and Cesariano, advanced the magic shadow art-science by writing scientific and experimental discussions of the subject. Somewhat later another Italian, Cardano, made another contribution.

Francesco Maurolico (Maurolycus), 1494-1575, a mathematician of Messina, and the great astronomer of his day, wrote *De Subtilitate,* about 1520, in which Pliny, Albertus Magnus, and Leonardo da Vinci are mentioned. The material included a mathematical, rather than experimental, discussion of light, mirrors and light theatres. This last subject shows that the use of light and shadow for theatrical purposes was being rapidly advanced. In 1521, Maurolico was said to have finished *Theoremata de lumine et umbra ad perspectivam et radiorum incidentiam facientia,* which was published in 1611 at Naples and in 1613 at Leyden. This book explained how a compound microscope could be fashioned. Men were now learning how to use lenses and how to make better ones so necessary for satisfactory projection of images.

Proposition 20 of the book was entitled "An object's shadow can be converted and projected." The author pointed out that if an object between a light and an opening is moved one way its shadow appears to move the other. He then went on to explain the reasons for Aristotle's square hole and round sun. He also showed accurately the relation of images and objects which was

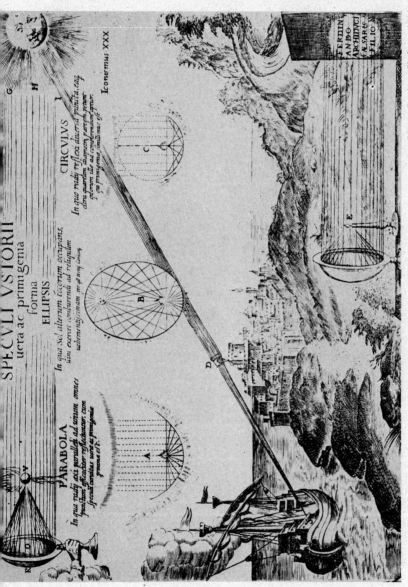

Ars Magna Lucis et Umbrae, 1646

BURNING GLASSES of Archimedes were ancient optical devices. They were used in the defense of Syracuse in 212 B. C. Some type of glass or lens is required in every camera or projector.

LEONARDO DA VINCI, famed Renaissance painter and sculptor, explained how to use the camera and described its relationship to the human eye.

fundamental for understanding how to focus lenses and mirrors.

Later astronomers credit Maurolico with having described the application of the *camera obscura* method to an observation of eclipses (but this was done for the first recorded time by Bacon or his contemporaries). Maurolico knew the works of Bacon and John Peckham, another English Franciscan monk of the 13th century, and studied both carefully. In 1535 he wrote *Cosmographia* and in later life studied the rays of light that make the phenomenon of the images appearing in a *camera obscura,* or any camera, possible without mentioning the apparatus or device or describing it. Being a mathematician primarily he was interested in that side of the problem and was not a practical demonstrator or showman.

Cesare Cesariano, an architect, painter and writer on art, made a reference to a light and shadow device which curiously has never been adequately explained. Cesariano was born in Milan in 1483 and died there on March 30, 1543. In 1528 he became architect to Carlo V and in 1533 architect to the city of Milan. In 1521 he designed the beautiful cathedral of Como.

While at Como, Cesariano prepared a translation and commentary on the *Architectura* of Vitruvius, architect to Emperor Augustus, whose classic on the subject was rediscovered in the 15th century. Vitruvius' book included a chapter on "Acoustic Properties of a Theatre"—a good subject for study even today. Cesariano's edition was published at Como in 1521 with a note saying that after the sudden departure of the translator and commentator from Como the work was finished by Bruono Mariro and Benedetto Giovio. It was considered a marvelous work, to be in the vernacular and not in Latin. At this period people wanted to have books in their own language and not in Latin.

While commenting on the word, *spectaculum,* translated as a "sighting tube", Cesariano described how a Benedictine monk and architect, Don Papnutio or Panuce, made a little sighting tube and fitted it into a small hole made for the purpose in a door. It was so arranged that no light could enter the room except through the small tube. The result was that outside objects were seen, with their own colors, in what really was a natural camera system. Of course, the images were upside down, as in any camera, without a special lens arrangement, but this fact was not noted by Cesariano.

The whole matter is perplexing. What is described is a "dark room" camera which, as has been observed, was never actually invented or discovered and was known for centuries. This Benedictine monk and architect may have made some refinements by carefully fitting the small opening to admit the light but that is all. At about this time, or a little earlier, the principles of the camera were set down by Leonardo da Vinci. The writer and other researchers have not been able to discover any trace of Benedettano Don Papnutio or Panuce. He certainly did not write any books or his name would be known to history and it would be possible to find more information about him and his work. There is no record of him in the Benedictine bibliography. Guillaume Libri, Italian writer, who worked in Paris in the 19th century and, incidentally, was charged with stealing da Vinci's manuscripts, said, "I have not so far been able to ascertain who Don Panuce was, or when he lived." Libri asserted that at any rate Leonardo's observation of the *camera obscura* must have been made before Cesariano saw or heard about this monk. However, Cesariano seems to have the record for the first published account of how to make a workable *camera obscura*.

Girolamo or Hieronimo Cardano (1501-1576) was an Italian physician and mathematician who has been described by Cajori, the mathematical historian, as "a singular mixture of genius, folly, self-conceit and mysticism." He lectured in medicine at the Universities of Milan, Paris and Bologna. In 1571, after having been, according to some, jailed for debt the year before, he was pensioned by the Pope and went to Rome to continue special work in medicine.

Cardano's contribution to motion picture pre-history was made in his *De Subtilitate,* published at Nuremberg in 1550. He showed how a concave mirror could be used to produce quite a wonderful show:—"If you wish to see what is happening on the street, put a small round glass at the window when the sun is bright and after the window has been shut one can see dim images on the opposite wall." He went on to explain how the images could be doubled, then quadrupled and how other strange appearances of things and one's self could be devised with a concave mirror. He remarked that the images appeared upside down. This, of course, is another description of the *camera obscura,* with a few additional points for recreational and instructional purposes.

It will be noted that Cardano's description is very like those of Bacon, Leonardo and Cesariano.

Now da Vinci's camera, the original "dark room" camera and progenitor of the modern pin-hole box camera, was ready for showmen to turn it to successful uses. Just after the middle of the 16th century, a young Neapolitan was prepared to spread the knowledge of the sporting use of the device throughout the world.

IV

PORTA, FIRST SCREEN SHOWMAN

↩ *Porta, a Neapolitan, blends fancy and showmanship for magic shadow entertainments in the 16th century—Barbaro and Benedetti put a lens in the "pin-hole" camera or* camera obscura.

THE FIRST CONTACT of the new dramatic art, then being developed in Europe and especially in England, with the magic shadow medium was made by a remarkable Neapolitan, Giovanni Battista della Porta.

Porta, a boy wonder, who would have felt at home in the modern Hollywood, put the room camera to theatrical uses. In a way Porta was both the last of the necromancers, who used lens and mirror devices to deceive, and the first legitimate screen writer and producer of light and shadow plays with true entertainment values.

Porta was born in Naples about the year 1538. He and his brother, Vincenzo, were educated by their uncle Adriano Spatafore, a learned man. The uncle had considerable wealth, which enabled young Porta to travel extensively and have the best available instructors. From boyhood Porta's chief interests were the stage and magic.

At an early age he started writing for the theatre and his comedies are rated with the best produced in Italy in the 16th century. But even before he began his professional writing for the stage, he had developed an interest in magic and anything approaching the magical. This avocation was developed during the rest of his life.

Porta was very fond of secrets and secret societies, founding the Academy of Secrets at Naples. He was also a member of the Roman Academy of the Lynxes, scientific society founded in 1603 —named for its trademark. Even magic inks for secret writing were an attraction to him.

For years it was generally believed that Porta invented the *camera obscura* but, as we have seen, it was known long before he was born. At the time of the discovery of photography Porta's title to the invention of the camera was discussed and it was definitely established that while he made some refinements and, of course, devised some special uses, he had nothing to do with its invention.

When about 15, Porta began the investigations which led to the writing of *Magia Naturalis, sive de Miraculis Rerum Naturalium,* "Natural Magic, or the wonders of natural things." The material was published five years later, at Naples, in four "books", or large chapters. Through the years he increased his notes on the subject and in 1589 the work was printed in twenty chapters.

Porta's *Natural Magic* was a popular book, a best-seller of the day. It was first translated into English and published in London in 1658. It was also translated into many other languages. *Natural Magic* contains a wide variety of subjects, including developments in the light and shadow art-science. Porta published the first detailed explanation of the construction and use of the *camera obscura* in the fourth "book".

"A system by which you can see, in their own colors, in the darkness objects outdoors lighted by the sun," was Porta's title for the section. He continued:

> If anyone wishes to see this effect, all the windows should be closed, and it would be helpful if the cracks were sealed so that no light may enter to ruin the show. Then in one window make a small opening in the form of a cone with the sun at the base and facing the room. Whiten the walls of the room or cover them with white linen or paper. In this way you will see all things outside lighted by the sun, as those walking in the streets, as if their feet were upwards, the right and left of the objects will be reversed and all things will seem interchanged. And the further the screen is from the opening, proportionately the larger the objects will appear;

the closer the paper screen or tablet, is drawn to the hole, the smaller the objects will appear.

Porta also had an explanation of the persistence of vision, so far as it was then understood. As an example, he mentioned that after walking in the bright sun it is difficult to discern objects in the darkness, until our eyes become accustomed to the change—and then we can see clearly in the dim light. To see the natural colors, Porta proposed the use of a concave mirror as the screen for the camera images. He then discussed phenomena resulting from the principal focus of the mirror. He tried to use the parallel to show how we see things rightside up instead of upside down. But his knowledge was not sufficient for that purpose, for he held that the seat of vision was at the center of the eye, as the focus of a concave mirror or lens system. In this he was not correct, according to modern experiments, but at least it was a plausible theory.

As a third point in his description of uses of the natural camera Porta said, "Anyone not knowing how to draw can outline the form of any object through the means of a stylus." Here was Alberti's *camera lucida,* or the camera adopted for the use of painters and designers. Porta instructed his readers to learn the colors of the object and then when it was thrown on the screen it would be easy to trace and paint in natural colors. He pointed out another interesting and important fact—a candle or lamp could be used as the light source instead of the sun.

Porta concluded his account of 1558 with an assertion that the system could be used to deceive and to do tricks through the aid of other devices. His last words on the subject were confusing: "Those who have attempted these experiments have produced nothing but trifles, and I do not think it has been invented by anyone else up to now." Earlier in his account he mentioned that he was now revealing what he thought should be kept a secret.

Roger Bacon, Alberti and Leonardo da Vinci and others were figuratively watching Porta when he wrote those lines and made those experiments. Even the same words about seeing people on the streets outside go back to Bacon, at least; and the use of the camera for drawing to Alberti and Leonardo. It is not clear whether or not Porta actually wished his readers to believe that he had invented the *camera obscura* which he described or that he had merely found some interesting applications. Perhaps he wanted the whole matter considered a secret.

But though Porta borrowed from the ancients without giving them credit, he deserves praise for publishing descriptions, following tests which he himself must have made. As in all sciences, the prehistory of the motion picture had experimenters and popularizers—and not infrequently the two functions were separated by a considerable period.

The developments claimed by Porta in the second edition of *Natural Magic* published in 1589 had been described previously by others. Once again he was a copier and popularizer rather than an inventor and discoverer. And that seems proper for a man who was by profession a playwright with a hobby interest in secret things, especially those relating to natural phenomena.

During the three decades prior to 1589, important developments were made in the science of optics. Both Barbaro and Benedetti described *camera obscura* systems fitted with lenses to improve the images, and E. Danti, an editor and translator, explained in 1573 how an upright, instead of an upside down, image could be shown through the use of a lens-mirror system.

Monsignor Daniello Barbaro published at Venice, in 1568, *La Pratica della Perspettiva,* "The Practice of Perspective", a book on optics. He describes the instrument designed by Alberti, the *camera lucida,* and gives an illustration of it. As in the case of Benedetti, Barbaro's chief title to memory is that he introduced the projection lens to the natural camera, thereby enlarging its scope. Without any lenses even a modern camera would give only inferior results and motion pictures would not be practical. It is also said Barbaro introduced the diaphragm, which is very important as a means of controlling the light in the camera.

Giovanni Battista Benedetti, a patrician of Venice, 1530-90, published at Turin a book called *Diversarum Speculationum Mathematicarum et Physicarum Liber,* "A Book of Various Mathematical and Physical Speculations", in which was included the first complete and clear description of the *camera obscura* equipped with a lens. The date of the volume was 1585, four years before Porta published his revised edition.

Benedetti used a double convex lens. His first knowledge of optics came from a study of Archimedes, whom he admired greatly. But his learning was not confined to optics. He influenced the great Descartes in geostatics, studying the laws of inertia and making the contribution of the path taken by a body going off from a revolving circle, i.e., tangent. In 1553 he reported that bodies in a vacuum fall with the same velocity.

Benedetti's description of the *camera obscura* included details on how to make the images appear upright. The material is contained in a printed letter to Pierro de Arzonis. First Benedetti discusses light and the fact that a greater light overshadows a smaller, "just as by day the stars cannot be seen." He then pointed out that if the light were controlled in a camera the outside images could be seen, but if the rays of the sun were allowed to enter (as by making the opening hole too large) then the images would "more or less vanish according to the strength or weakness of the solar rays."

Benedetti continued:

I do not wish to keep any remarkable effect of this system a secret from you . . . the round opening the size of one small mirror may be filled in with one of those spectacles which are made for old people (but not the kind for those of short sight), but one whose both surfaces are convex, not concave. Then set up a white sheet of paper (as the screen), so far back from the opening that the objects on the outside may appear on it. And if indeed these outside objects are illuminated by the sun they will be seen so clearly and distinctly that nothing will seem to be more beautiful or more delightful. The only objection is that the objects will appear inverted. But if we wish to see those objects upright, this can be done best by interposing another plane mirror.

In the revised and expanded edition of his *Natural Magic,* Porta gave a more complete description of the uses of the camera. Part of the text was identical with the earlier accounts; part was new.

Porta had learned how to make his opening in the single window better by this time—"make the opening a palm's size in width and breadth and glue over this a sheet of lead or bronze which has in the middle an opening about the size of a finger." He next pointed out that the outside objects can be seen clearer

Ars Magna Lucis et Umbrae, 1646

CAMERA OBSCURA, *the natural room camera, was accidentally discovered in antiquity, probably in the Far East. Here is shown an improved version by Giovanni Battista della Porta, 16th Century Neopolitan writer, scientist and showman. A translucent sheet was the screen. The images were upside down and indistinct as no lenses were used. Artists and entertainers found the apparatus of value.*

Nil dat, quod nitil est!
Jo: Kepler

Wissenschaftliche Abhandlungen, 1878

JOHANNES KEPLER *developed the scientific principles of the camera and its use in astronomy.*

and sharper if a crystalline lens is put in the opening of the camera as suggested by Barbaro and Benedetti. Porta also mentioned that the insertion of another mirror in the system would make the images appear upright instead of upside down.

But Porta showed himself a real showman by his final word—describing how hunting, battles and other illusions may be made to appear in a room. Here artificial objects and painted scenes were substituted for the natural outdoors as the pictures for the room camera in a method originally suggested by Alberti. Porta said, "Nothing can be more pleasing for important people, dilettants and connoisseurs to behold."—An early premiere audience of invited guests!

Porta recommended the use of miniature models of animals and natural scenes, the first stage sets for "motion pictures," with puppet-like characters. He wrote, "Those present in the show-room will behold the trees, animals, hunters and other objects without knowing whether they are true or only illusions." Porta revealed that he had put on shows of this kind many times for his friends and the illusions of reality were so good that the delighted audience could scarcely be told how the effects were achieved. He also told how the audience could be terrified.

Porta concluded this account with a description of how to use the camera in order to observe an eclipse, something which Bacon or one of his contemporaries had already worked out. Before good instruments were developed, the room camera was an excellent device to save the astronomer's eyesight and still give him a good view of an eclipse. The giant 200-inch telescope at Palomar in California is closely related to the original use of the camera for astronomical work.

There does not seem to be any evidence that Porta developed a portable camera, the direct ancestor of the modern photographic camera. He also did not appear to have much success with his lenses, as he found the concave mirrors as good as or better than a *camera obscura* with a lens.

The general subject of the chapter which included the camera was "Herein Are Propounded Burning Glasses" "and the Wonderful Sights to be Seen by Them." (Recall Archimedes and his Burning Glasses.) Let Porta tell it: "What could be seen more wonderful, than that by reciprocal strokes of reflexion, images should appear outwardly hanging in the air and yet neither the visible object nor the glass seen? that they may seem not to be repercussions of the glasses, but spirits of vain phantasms."

In a book on refraction, published in 1593, the eye and the *camera obscura* were compared by Porta. He also covered refraction, vision, the rainbow, prismatic colors (all subjects treated by the early experimenters in optics).

Porta had a great, though mixed, influence. Even in his own mind he did not seem able to decide whether the magic shadows should be used to deceive the public as effects of secret powers or whether they should be used for genuine entertainment and instruction.

After Porta, the "dark chamber" was developed for the use of painters and artists in England and on the continent.

V

KEPLER AND THE STARS

⌐ *Kepler, German astronomer, devel-*
ops the scientific principles of the camera
obscura *and applies magic shadows to*
the stars of the heavens—Scheiner and
D'Aguilon improve image devices.

JOHANNES KEPLER, the great astronomer, advanced the art-
science of magic shadows by developing the theory of the
projection of images as well as the scientific use of multiple lenses
and the *camera obscura* or "dark chamber". Da Vinci told how the
camera could be used; Porta tried it out for entertainment on a
considerable scale but there still was need for penetrating attention
from a scientist. That Kepler supplied.

Kepler was a precocious child though he suffered from poor
health. He had no special interest or inclination towards astronomy
until in 1594, at the age of 23, he found himself required to
teach a class in that subject. Soon he became an expert and before
his death announced the Kepler laws explaining the planetary
system. In 1600 Kepler became assistant to Tycho Brahe (1546-
1601), the greatest practical astronomer to that date but one
who rejected the Copernican theory that the earth and planets
revolve around the sun, a theory which was firmly proved by
Kepler. Brahe lost the tip of his nose in a duel, so he wore a gold
one, carrying with him cement with which to stick on the tip
whenever it fell off.

A few years after becoming astronomer to the Emperor,
Kepler published, in 1604, *Ad Vitellionem Paralipomena*—
"Supplement to Witelo"; Witelo, a Pole called Thuringopolonus,

wrote a treatise on optics about 1270. He was a contemporary of Roger Bacon. Kepler used da Vinci's parallel of the eye and the room camera and set the latter's principles on a firm scientific basis.

Kepler wrote, "This art, according to my knowledge, was first handed down by Giovanni Battista Porta and was one of the chief parts of his *Natural Magic*." (But, as the reader recalls, Porta was not the first to know about the *camera obscura* and was not its inventor but only a popularizer.) "But content with a practical experience," Kepler continued, "Porta did not add a scientific demonstration. Yet only by the use of this device can astronomers study the image of the solar eclipse."

Kepler then described the *camera obscura* or "dark chamber," adding an interesting observation. He proposed that the spectator should keep out of the daylight for fifteen minutes or a half hour before he planned to use the camera so that he could get his eyes accustomed to the darkness in order to observe the images more clearly. Kepler then instructed that the objects to be represented should be placed in bright light, either of the sun or lamps. He also noted that the objects were reversed, and remarked that the images appeared in the colors of the objects. Kepler also explained that a diaphragm was needed to control the amount of light admitted to the camera, and that best results were obtained when the sun was near the horizon.

A detailed and rather technical explanation of how the camera system works was given by Kepler. Towards the end of the description he wrote an important instruction: "All the walls of the camera except the one used as the screen for the images should be black." This was necessary to prevent reflection and dulling of the brilliance of the images on the white wall or screen. Everyone knows how the insides of a modern camera are black for the very same purpose. Kepler also noted that the "camera" must be tightly sealed. He was the first to refer to the device under the simple name of "camera" which in time was adopted universally.

Kepler also was the first to give a sound theory of vision. (Recall the shot-from-eye or shot-from-object schools of the ancients.) Kepler stated, "Seeing amounts to feeling the stimulus of the retina which is painted with colored rays of the visible world. The picture must then be transmitted to the brain by a mental current and delivered at the seat of the visual faculty." That is a rather good definition even by modern standards. Kepler, however, was not 100 per cent correct. He held that light had an infinite velocity. To Kepler goes the credit for being the first correctly to explain after-images, a knowledge of which is so vital to understanding how the illusion of motion is created.

Kepler started to use a telescope about 1609 and through its use he was able to develop improved ideas for the room camera by the time he published his *Dioptrice,* "Concerning Lenses," a foundation of modern optics, in 1611. In that work the basis was first established for what was later to be long-range or "telescope" photography which makes possible many important effects in the modern motion picture.

The telescope, the most highly developed lens system and the reverse of a projection arrangement, was invented in Holland in the early part of the 17th century. Galileo, who with Kepler did much to popularize the telescope, admitted that he had seen one made by a Dutchman before he fashioned his own.

The name "telescope" was coined by Damiscian of the Italian scientific "Academy of the Lynxes," to which Porta also had belonged. The invention of the telescope is commonly credited to "the spectacle maker of Middleburgh," usually identified as Hans Lippershey. The compound microscope, effects of which had been indicated by Roger Bacon, evidently also was invented a few years prior to the telescope—by Zachary Janssen, in Holland. But it was first described in Italy. Early telescopes generally followed the model developed by Galileo, while by the middle of the 17th century the superiority of Kepler's method was recognized and larger and more powerful telescopes were possible. In recent times the telescope has reverted to a mirror—or Burning Glass—reflecting system instead of the standard style refracting telescope.

To a contemporary of Kepler goes the acclaim for being the first to use the *camera obscura* apart from a room; in other words, in a portable form. Thus was the first portable camera developed more than two hundred years before photography was invented. The man was Scheiner, another astronomer.

Christopher Scheiner, a German Jesuit, born about 1575 in Swabia, did much work in astronomy and perfected various ingenious optical instruments. Some say he was the first to use the camera projection device for throwing the sun's image on a screen in order to study its details. This replaced a system which used colored glasses. Kepler, prior to this, suggested the method but it is generally acknowledged that Scheiner made the first application. In 1610 Scheiner invented his Pantograph or optical copying instrument. In March, 1611, he observed sun spots. His superiors were afraid that he and they would be exposed to ridicule if he were to publish such a discovery under his own name—it was so opposed to the contemporary scientific as well as traditional scientific belief. And so his findings were published in 1612 by a friend, under an assumed name.

Scheiner was a believer in the need for accuracy in experiments to form a firm basis for future development of theory. He studied the eye and believed that the retina was the seat of vision. By the year 1616 he had so attracted attention of scientists that the Archduke Maximilian invited him to Innsbruck. Scheiner taught mathematics and Hebrew and continued his work in optics. He was the author of *Rosa Ursina,*—1626-30, the standard work on the sun for generations. In 1623 he was a professor of mathematics at the Roman College, where Kircher fell under his personal influence. The last years of Scheiner's life were spent at Neisse in Silesia, where he died in 1650.

Scheiner was influenced by François d'Aguilon, the first of several Jesuits who made an important contribution to what was to be the modern motion picture. D'Aguilon advanced the knowledge of optics throughout Europe.

D'Aguilon was born in Brussels in 1566 and after entering the Jesuits in 1586 and being educated he became a professor of philosophy at the famous college in Douai, France. Later he was head of the College of Antwerp. D'Aguilon did not confine his interests to philosophy and speculative knowledge alone but was very much interested in certain sciences, notably optics. Moreover, he was a practicing architect and probably designed the Jesuit church at Antwerp.

His work on optics, published at Antwerp in 1613, was famous. In it is found for the first time the expression "stereographic projection," which has survived to the present. This was known from the time of Hipparchus but had not received a permanent name until it was given by d'Aguilon, to whom must go part of the credit for the name of all devices with "stereo" somewhere in the title. D'Aguilon explored at length the subject of after-images. He correctly pointed out that the image physically disappears when the cause is removed (as a camera no longer "sees" after the shutter is closed) but there remains something impressed on the organ of sight, a certain effect on the sense of vision.

D'Aguilon was revising his book on optics when he died, in 1617. One edition was published in Antwerp in 1685 with the title *Opticorum Libri Sex*. Perhaps he was on the eve of the great discovery which was to be made in a few years by one of his successors. However, to him goes the credit for the name which was attached for centuries to all kinds of shadow-plays, and is still known today—Stereoscopic.

By the first quarter of the 17th century the camera was widely used for the observation of the greatest light and shadow show—the universe with sun, moon and stars. Experiments also had been made, by Porta and others, in the entertainment possibilities of the "dark chamber." The stage was ready for the man who would bring about projection, as we know it, with the magic lantern. A long step would then be taken towards realizing man's instinctive ambition to capture and recreate life for entertainment and instructive purposes.

VI

KIRCHER'S 100th ART

⤳Kircher's magic lantern projects pictures and the art of screen presentation is born—First screen picture show in Rome, 1646 — Kircher's book, Ars Magna Lucis et Umbrae, *tells the world how.* ⤚

IN THE SECOND quarter of the 17th Century the stage was set for the birth of the magic lantern, progenitor of all cinematographic projectors. The chief actor was a German, a fellow countryman of Kepler and of many other serious scientists in the light and shadow field, but it was in Italy, native land of many arts and showmen, of Leonardo da Vinci and of Porta, that he worked. The man was Athanasius Kircher.

The age in which Kircher worked was a difficult period. The Thirty Years War ravaged Europe from 1618 to 1648 and the people suffered more than at any period down to our own. Europe politically was in chaos as after World Wars I and II. Only in literature and science were there signs of hope and promise. The eyes of many thoughtful Europeans turned away from the Old World to the new lands across the sea.

Kircher was born five years before the first permanent English settlement in the New World. But let him tell us in the words of his Latin autobiography, parts of which, it is believed, are here translated into English for the first time: "At the third hour after midnight on the second of May in the year 1602, I was brought into the common air of disaster at Geysa, a town which is a three hours' journey from Fulda." (Not far from the modern Frankfurt-

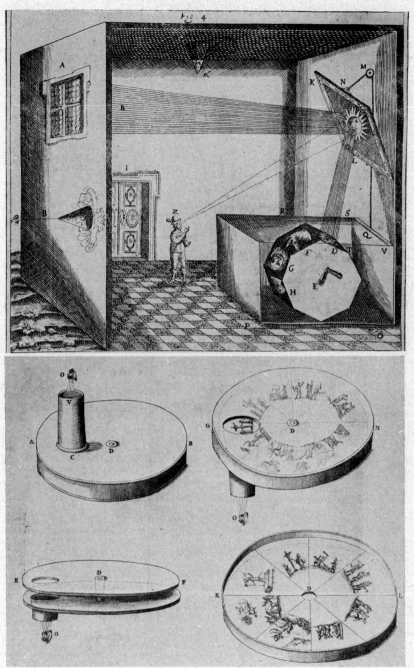

Ars Magna Lucis et Umbrae, 1646-1671

PICTURE WHEELS invented by Kircher. Above, rotating giant wheel caused one picture to succeed another. Below, story telling disk.

MAGIC LANTERN, *Kircher's projector, the original stereopticon. The screen images were crude silhouettes but the projector included the essential elements.*

Ars Magna Lucis et Umbrae. 1671

on-Main, Germany.) "When I was six days old I was dedicated to Athanasius by my parents, John Kircher and Anna Gansekin, Catholics and servants of God and workers of good deeds, because I was born on that Saint's Feast Day."

Kircher thus described his father, mother and the family: "John Kircher was a very great scholar and a doctor of philosophy. When the report of his learning and wisdom came to the Prince," (probably Rudolph), "he was summoned and made a member of the council at Fulda. Later he was put in charge of the fortress of Haselstein because he had been diligent in destroying the printing machines of the heretics. He married a maiden of Fulda, Anna, daughter of an honest citizen named Gansekin. Nine children, six boys and three girls, were born to them. All the boys entered one of the several religious orders. Of all these I was the youngest and smallest."

Kircher's father was a man of influence and learning, though evidently not of noble birth. He had studied philosophy and theology but was not a religious, though he did teach for a time in a Benedictine monastery. Very likely he was a stern parent. The mother, it would appear, was the daughter of a merchant or storekeeper and certainly was not learned like her husband. But no doubt she was more liberal and understanding.

Kircher's course of studies is interesting: "After the age of childhood, around the tenth year, I was placed in the elementary studies, at first at Music; then I was introduced to the elements of the Latin language." At that time Latin was still the universal language of scholarship. It is likely that Kircher spoke Latin much more than any other language. All his writing was in Latin, though in time he became a talented linguist.

Kircher's father sent him to the Jesuit college at Fulda, because he wanted his youngest son to learn Greek in addition to Latin and in time to become a universal scholar. Kircher's teacher at Fulda was John Altink, S.J. The course followed the famous Jesuit *Ratio Studiorum,* which is still the basis of studies in the many hundreds of schools conducted by that order throughout the world. Then, as now, emphasis was on the classics. Somewhat later his father took him to a Rabbi "who taught me Hebrew," as Kircher wrote, "with the result that I was skilled in that language for the rest of my life."

At the same age as a high school graduate in the United States,

Kircher could read, write and speak Latin, Greek and Hebrew, in addition to German, and probably he also had a good foundation in French and Italian.

At the old town of Paderborn on October 2, 1618, Kircher entered the Society of Jesus, militant religious order founded by the Spaniard-soldier-churchman, Ignatius of Loyola, in 1540, and already a powerful influence in education in Europe and in missionary work even as far as India and Japan. Kircher did not enter the Jesuits as early as he had wished because he had fallen while ice-skating and had suffered an injury.

From 1618 to 1620, Kircher occupied himself with religious duties, spending the time largely in prayer. After 1620 he continued with the usual studies for the priesthood—philosophy and theology. He studied philosophy at Cologne and briefly taught at the Jesuit Colleges at Coblenz and Heiligenstadt. Along with these pursuits, Kircher took a special interest in languages and in mathematics, the foundation for all scientific work. He completed his studies in theology at Mainz and was ordained a priest in 1628.

Kircher was given ample opportunity to take courses, despite the troubled times resulting from the wars. In the year 1629, he was at Speyer where he expressed to his religious superior a preference for missionary work in China. Next he took an interest in Egyptian writing, hieroglyphics, which were not to be translated until many years later. Chaldean, Arabic and Samaritan were added to Kircher's language studies. Then for a short period he was professor of ethics and mathematics at the University of Würzburg.

In 1618, when Kircher had entered the Jesuits, the Thirty Years' War had broken out. Then, as in our own time, Germany was no place for serious studies. Kircher, after he became a priest, spent considerable time in France where the organization of a powerful central government was being undertaken by Richelieu. The Cardinal was a patron of the arts, founding the French Academy. It is likely that word of Kircher's learning reached Richelieu, for Kircher visited several of the colleges and universities in the south of France, stopping at Lyons and later at Avignon. Kircher continued all the while his remarkable studies, and began to write, publishing his first book in 1630.

Soon the fame of Kircher attracted the attention of the highest ecclesiastical and educational authorities. Pope Urban VIII, who had struggled in vain to prevent the Thirty Years' War, and Francesco Cardinal Barberini (nephew of Pope Urban), summoned Kircher to Rome late in 1633. Just before the word to come to Rome reached him, he was invited to Vienna by the Emperor Ferdinand. Kircher started for Austria by boat from a French port but was shipwrecked and the order to report to Rome reached him after his rescue.

The invitation to come to Rome could not be refused. But there is every reason to believe that Kircher was delighted to have the opportunity of working in Rome under such high auspices. The civil situation was somewhat more stable in Rome than in Germany. Furthermore Rome was the intellectual center as well as focal point of much political maneuvering. Ambassadors and special agents representing Richelieu of France, the King of Spain, the Emperor of Germany and many of the other European powers, great and small, were constantly coming and going, seeking to increase the power of the state they represented and their own prestige as well. The heads of all the religious orders lived in Rome and hence it was the headquarters for knowledge of new developments in science and of news from the lands being explored in America and in the Far East.

Kircher stood apart from these struggles for political, religious and educational power. As a Jesuit he had put aside prospects of ecclesiastical advancement. He was content with his studies, his teaching and his inventions. But others were not content to leave him in peace.

At the request of Cardinal Barberini, Kircher was made professor of mathematics at the Roman College which was then popular with the young Roman nobility and the learned from all over the world. While teaching, Kircher continued his work in the Oriental languages and mathematics and also branched out into the natural sciences.

Kircher was a little man of boundless energy and once interested in a problem was never content till he knew all the facts, from personal investigation if possible, and had written an exhaustive tome on the subject. He made many field trips to test theories and ideas by practical experience. An active exponent of experimental science, Kircher made important contributions to human knowledge, though some of his books contained not a little error, and even some nonsense.

Kircher's work with magic lanterns and his observations on
the magic shadow art-science were released to the educated world
in his *Ars Magna Lucis et Umbrae*—"The Great Art of Light
and Shadow"—published at Rome in 1646. Kircher defined his
"Great Art" as "the faculty by which we make and exhibit with
light and shadow the wonders of things in nature." That applies
to living pictures today as it did in the 17th Century. Even the
sound of the modern motion pictures is recorded and reproduced
through light and shadow action.

No clue is given by Kircher to the exact date he invented
the magic projection lantern. But it was probably not long before
he finished the book in 1644 or 1645. Kircher dedicated his thick
quarto volume, which was handsomely published by Herman
Scheus at the press of Ludovici Grignani in Rome, to Archduke
Ferdinand III, the Holy Roman Emperor, King of Hungary, King
of Bohemia and King of the Romans. Hence, knowledge of the
screen first appeared in print under very distinguished patronage.

The title page explained that the great art of light and shadow
had been "digested" into ten books "in which the wonderful
powers of light and shadow in the world and even in the natural
universe are shown and new forms for exhibiting the various
earthly uses are explained."

The Emperor wrote a foreword and this was followed by an
introduction of Kircher "to the reader." Kircher spoke of the
earlier use of light and shadow by the necromancers to deceive,
but pointed out that his developments were for "public use, or
a means of private recreation." Introductory material also included
several odes about the subject and the author, as well as the
necessary ecclesiastical approvals.

The first nine books, or long sections, of *Ars Magna Lucis et
Umbrae* include such diverse topics as the following: Light, reflection, images, the speaking tube, the structure of the eye, sketching
devices, the art of painting, geometrical patterns, clocks, the nature
of reflected light, refraction and means of measuring the earth.

The section which is of special interest in the story of magic
shadows is the tenth—it gives the title to the whole work. The
sub-title of the chapter is, "Wonders of light and shadow, in
which is considered the more hidden effects of light and shadow
and various applications." In the preface to the section Kircher

wrote "in this, as in our other research, we have believed that the results of our important experiments should be made public." "That risk is taken," he continued, "for the purpose of preventing the curious readers from being defrauded of time and money by those who sell imitation devices, for many have provided wondrous, rare, marvelous and unknown things and others have sold so much bunk."

The first section of the all-important tenth chapter discussed magic clocks and sun-dials; the second, the *camera obscura* or "dark chamber," lenses, telescopes, other optical devices. In the third section there appears the magic lantern. The section is called, "Magia Catoptrica, or concerning the wondrous exhibition of things by the use of a mirror." *Catoptron* in Greek means "mirror." Kircher wrote, "Magia catoptrica is nothing else but the method of exhibiting through the means of mirrors hidden things which seem to be outside the scope of the human mind." Ancient authorities who had made contributions to this art-science were mentioned by Kircher.

First Kircher explained how steel mirrors were made and polished—mirrors or reflectors are still of importance in gathering light in the motion picture projector. He commented on the various types of convex, concave, spherical and other types of mirrors.

In Kircher's day even the learned were quite uneducated according to modern standards, especially on all matters of physical science. Images that appeared from nowhere were most mysterious and few knew how they were produced. The telescope and microscope were still very new and many doubted what their eyes saw through these inventions.

Kircher, as a showman, described a Catoptric Theatre—a large cabinet in which many mirrors were concealed. One of the "Theatres" was placed in the Villa Borghese Palace in Rome and doubtless delighted the nobles of that day as much as the people in the United States were pleased with the first Edison peep-show machines in 1894. For Kircher's Catoptric Theatre was an early peep-show device. It also has a relation to the Kaleidoscope of the early 19th century.

The first form of the magic lantern described by Kircher was merely a lantern suitable for showing letters at a remote distance. It is very simple and appears entirely elementary. But the first step was taken. The third problem of the third section of the tenth

book of the *Ars Magna Lucis et Umbrae* was how to construct
such an artificial lantern with which written characters may be
shown at a remote distance.

The parts are easily distinguished—a concave mirror at the
rear; a candle for a light source; a handle and a place for inserting
silhouette letter slides. Kircher noted that in the device the flame
will burn with an unaccustomed brilliance. "Through the aid of
this device very small letters may be exhibited without any trouble." He noted that some will think there is an enormous fire, so
bright will the lantern shine. He added that the strength of the
light will be increased if the interior of the cylinder is covered with
an alloy of silver and lead to increase its reflecting qualities.

The second Kircher device of direct relation to the motion picture is his machine for creating metamorphoses or rapid changes.
All kinds of transformations could be shown. Here was first introduced the revolving wheel on which pictures were painted. It bears
an analogous relation to the motion picture devices of the early
19th century—also using a revolving vertical wheel. The modern
projector likewise has its film pictures on a small wheel or reel.

Kircher explained that in this catoptric machine a man looking
at the mirror (equivalent to the screen in a theatre) sees images
of a fire, a cow and other animals all blending one into another.
It is unlikely that the giant wheel could be revolved swiftly enough
to give anything like the proper illusion of motion but certainly
there was a transformation which must have appeared wondrous
and entertaining. (Illustration facing page 48.)

Kircher also described how images of objects could be projected
by means of the light of a candle. Through this system various
images were exhibited in a darkened chamber. But Kircher evidently was not satisfied with this method, for no illustration of it
appeared in the first edition of his book. The reason is obvious.
A candle could provide only enough illumination for the faintest
shadows. Kircher wrote that those objects which need only a
fraction of the sun's light can be shown by a candle in a small
room. Two methods for this were indicated: (1) with a concave
mirror reflecting the images and (2) projecting the image through
a lens. It was noted that the better single method was through the
lens. A combination of the two provided the most light. Kircher
remarked that he had read in a history of the Arabs that a certain
king of Bagdad used a mirror to work wonders in order to deceive

the people. He also pointed out that some men had used mirrors to project into dark places what the ignorant thought were devils.

The chief problem in Kircher's day and for centuries afterwards was to provide sufficient light. The final solution did not come until electric light was introduced. Probably Kircher's most efficient projection was one in which the sun was used as the source of light. Even in the early part of the 20th century arrangements were used which hooked up the sun with the magic lantern because it was thought that the results were even better and cheaper than those obtained with electric light.

Kircher's sun magic projector used a real optical system which is fundamental even to this day. There was first the source of light, then a reflector and the object, and the projected image. The effects, of course, would be most startling in a darkened room. Kircher also showed how shadows of any type of figure could be thrown onto a wall or screen through the same method.

In those days when there was much secret correspondence and keen interest in various forms of cipher, many of Kircher's readers were glad to note how the magic lantern could be used for such a purpose. At that time people would not, it was believed, detect that the letters in such a system were simply backwards and upside down. The message could be read easily by projecting images of the letters. The same result could be had by turning the paper upside down and holding it before a mirror.

After listing these many diverse uses of the magic lantern system Kircher thought it well to conclude his book lest he be charged with "meandering" endlessly on a subject which some would consider trivial. Kircher said, "We leave all these to the talented reader for further refinement. A word to the wise is sufficient. Innumerable things could be said concerning the application of this device but we leave to others new material of invention and lest this work grow too long we cut off the thread of discussion about these devices."

Kircher ended his entire book by saying that it was published "not for income or glory but for the common good."

In his Latin autobiography Kircher made only one passing reference to his *Ars Magna Lucis et Umbrae,* "The Great Art of Light and Shadow."

Let Kircher speak:

At this time (around 1645) three more books were published, the first on the magnetic art, *On Magnetism;* another *On the Great Art of Light and Shadow* and a third written in the name of *Musurgia,* "Music." These are not insignificant works, praise be God. They occasioned applause but this applause soon brought me another form of tribulation; new accusations piled up and for this reason my critics said I should devote my whole life to developing mathematics. So with desperate hope on account of this impenetrable difficulty I gave up my work on hieroglyphics and my heart and mind were discouraged.

At one point in the discussion of the magic lantern in *Ars Magna Lucis et Umbrae* Kircher interrupted the thread of the story long enough to point out that charges of the use of the black arts had been made against him and others who knew the use of mirrors and lenses by some who had no knowledge of philosophy and science. He told how Roger Bacon was charged with necromancy because he could show a recognizable shadow of himself in a dark room where his friends were assembled. Kircher noted that certainly a talented philosopher and scientist could accomplish all these effects through skill in the use of mirrors and lenses and without any trace of the suspect black art.

The charge of necromantic art was the source of much of Kircher's unhappiness. Some considered him in league with the devil because he could make images and shadows and objects appear where none had been before. It was the age-old story that some in the audience or among the readers did not understand how an effect was produced so its validity and legitimacy were denied.

Praise and blame always have been the lot of discoverers and inventors.

Kircher had, however, better fortune than many others. He was able to write in his autobiography, "Divine Providence, which never fails us, took care of my trouble in this wonderful way—my appointed work was restored to me and by the occasion of this good fortune I escaped the traps of my adversaries."

Adversaries on even scientific matters in those days battled to the death. What happened was this: A commission established by Innocent X, who had been elected Pope in 1644, ordered that Kircher be allowed to continue his beloved antiquarian studies. It seemed that the Obelisk of Caracalla had been partially destroyed and Kircher was given the task of directing the restoration. Kircher's original patron, Cardinal Barberini, continued to have influence, being Pope Innocent's legate or ambassador to the Emperor.

And so the man who had done so much to advance the art-science of living pictures for the knowledge and enjoyment of vast millions in the centuries to come spent the happiest days of his life looking towards the dead and buried past.

A quarter of a century later, Kircher was able to revise and enlarge his book on *The Great Art of Light and Shadow* and have it printed in a great folio edition in 1671 by John Jansson of Waesberge at Amsterdam. Conditions had changed greatly—Kircher was no longer a newcomer at Rome, suspected of being in league with the devil on account of his powers with mirrors and lenses and his amazing projected images. His fame as a universal scholar, "The Doctor of a Hundred Arts," had spread throughout the European world. Men now had begun to realize there was much of great value in his *Magia Catoptrica* or Magic Projection with mirrors.

Jacob Alban Ghibbesim, M.D., professor at the Roman College, in the caption for Kircher's portrait, used these words: "This man and his name are known to the ends of the earth."

In 1670 Kircher had a new patron, John Frederic, to whom he dedicated his work. The Emperor Ferdinand, who sponsored the first edition, had died in 1657. Europe was gradually recovering from the effects of the Thirty Years' War. Louis XIV was establishing an all-powerful personal rule in France. Holland and Switzerland were jealously guarding their newly won independence. Sweden was an important European power. Great Britain had a short-lived republic under Cromwell. In the New World the English had consolidated their position by driving the Dutch out of New Amsterdam, occupying New York in 1664. Much of the New World had yet to be explored.

"Vagabonds and imposters" had carried the magic lantern everywhere during the quarter century following its announcement, usually claiming it as their own invention. Kircher thought the time had come for him to set down in more detail various additional applications of his magic lantern, invented 30 years before. The only additions Kircher made to the entire tome were in the section on the magic lanterns. Two new plates were made, showing room and box-type projectors and also added was another special plate on a particular application demonstrating that Kircher used the lantern idea to tell a story. (Illustration facing page 49.)

Let Kircher now explain about Walgenstein, a Dane, one of his first and most successful imitators in the practice of the magic lantern:

> Concerning the construction of Magic Lantern or Thaumaturga (Wonder Projector)—
>
> Although we have already mentioned this lantern in several places and shown a method of transmitting images by the sun into dark places, we will illustrate one further use—that is, a method of projecting painted images of objects in their own colors. Because previously we merely outlined this subject and left it entirely apart from other more important inventions, it happened that many who were drawn by the novelty of the magic lantern applied their minds to its refinement.
>
> First among these was a Dane, Thomas Walgenstein, not a little known as a mathematician, who, recalling my invention, produced a better form of the lantern which I had described. These he sold, with great profit to himself, to many of the prominent people of Italy. He sold so many that by now the magic lantern is nearly commonplace in Rome. However, there is none among all these lanterns which differs from the lantern described by us. Walgenstein said that with this lantern model he showed a large number of sufficiently bright and shining pictures in a dark chamber and they aroused the greatest admiration in the audiences. We in our dark chamber at the college are accustomed to show many new pictures to the greatest wonder of those looking on. The show is most worthwhile seeing, the subjects being either satire or tragic plays, all the pictures in the appearances of the living.

From Kircher's statement Walgenstein should be hailed as the first commercializer of the projector and the first traveling picture showman or "road-show man." Unfortunately, little is known of this man. While he may have been "not a little known" in Kircher's time, he left no mark on history, evidently never writing a book or holding an educational or other position which would have been recorded. It seems certain that he was the Dane of whom the French inventor and scientist, Milliet de Chales, spoke about as introducing the magic lantern in Lyons, France, some years after it was invented by Kircher.

Kircher's statement about the shows which he put on at the Roman College is most interesting. The reference to tragic and comic plays indicates beyond doubt that Kircher used a succession of lantern slides to tell a story as the modern motion picture is made up of a succession of pictures.

Kircher included a description of the slide projector so that all who wished could imitate his work. "All these things have been shown so that the reader can make his own," he said. "The work of art formerly described does not differ from the new lantern." He pointed out that moving slides had been added so that the objects might appear with the aspect of living shadows. He again explained how a concave mirror and diaphragm should be used. Kircher informed his readers that he usually used four or five slides, each having eight pictures painted on glass. The illustrations, he noted, explain the system better than words. We echo that and refer the reader to the illustrations of the box and room moving-slide projectors of Kircher.

Kircher in his 1671 edition described a form of revolving disc to tell a story. (He selected the most widely known story of all for the model—The Life of Christ.) The light available would not give a great effect but the pattern was set. Nearly two hundred years later the first projection of motion pictures was to be achieved with a somewhat similar disc and series of painted figures. Kircher's revolving disc told the story with a series of still pictures rapidly succeeding each other. (Illustration facing page 48.)

By explaining all details of the method and construction of the magic lantern to everyone interested, Kircher had hoped to expose some of the imposters who were using his invention to arouse fear and make the people believe that the operator had magic powers.

Kircher, with his "hundred arts," became *vir toto orbe celebratissimus*—a man well known throughout the world—according to Jerome Langenmantel who edited his autobiography in 1684. However, since his own era Kircher has been relatively unknown.

There was hardly a branch of learning that did not attract Kircher's attention. He assembled one of the best ethnological collections of his time. He attempted to develop a basic language and was one of the first to make a start towards deciphering hieroglyphics. In the field of magnetism he was a pioneer and in 1632 was one of the first to map compass variation and ocean currents.

In medicine Kircher was a proponent of the new and generally disbelieved germ theory of disease, and an experimenter in the use of hypnotism for healing purposes. He contributed much to the early knowledge of volcanoes. An an inventor, Kircher perfected one of the first counting machines, speaking tubes, Aeolian harps and developed the microscope to an enlarging power of 1,000 diameters.

However, despite all his knowledge, his title of "Doctor of a Hundred Arts" and the trouble and fame incidental to the invention of the magic lantern—his least art, or "the hundredth"—Kircher was not prideful of his reputation. He concluded his little autobiography by describing himself as "a poor, humble and unworthy servant of God." His heart was buried in a shrine to Mary, the Mother of God, which Kircher had constructed on the Sabine Hill in Rome.

*

The art-science of projection and the magic lantern were further explained through the publication of three other books which included a description of Kircher's work and illustrations of his projector systems; namely, George de Valesius' volume on the Museum of the Roman College in 1678, which pointed out that Kircher had developed magic lanterns using one or more lenses, and that several different models were on display and in use since the time of their invention; Johann Stephan Kesler's book on Kircher's experiments published in 1680 and another edition in 1686; and finally there was published in Rome in 1707, a work on the Kircher Museum—the Museum of the Roman College which had by then been given officially the name of its collector. Today only a few small objects remain of Kircher's original collections. Unfortunately, Kircher's devices were destroyed shortly after his death.

The museum of Kircher at the Roman College, the first picture theatre in the world, was an amazing place. Every conceivable kind of antiquarian and scientific object was assembled—from Egyptian inscriptions to stuffed animals, fish, rare stones, curiosities from the New Worlds and everything pertaining to the pursuits of the "Doctor of a Hundred Arts." Any spectator, from one of the eminent Cardinals to a young Roman nobleman and student at the College who was invited to a performance, would certainly have been well prepared for an extraordinary show after looking at the diverse collections at the museum.

In the 17th century there was no doubt as to the identity of the inventor of the magic lantern. Before Kircher's death in 1680 his magic lantern was widely used in Europe for scientific and entertainment purposes as well as for the art of deception. The question was raised by later writers seeking to claim a national of their own country as the inventor. Kesler wrote in 1680, "In the catoptric art images are exhibited in dark places through the magic lantern which our author (Kircher) invented and which, to his undying memory, he communicated to the world."

In those days some men liked to keep secret their inventions lest some one else claim the rewards. Two and a half centuries later, Thomas A. Edison sometimes found it better not to take out foreign patents on his inventions because that frequently served only as notice to those who sought to duplicate his work. For this reason Edison did not spend the $150 necessary to obtain foreign patents on his moving picture cameras and viewers.

VII

POPULARIZING KIRCHER'S PROJECTOR

⌐ Kircher's magic lantern is popular-
ized by others — Schott — Milliet de
Chales—Zahn—Molyneux—The name
and fame of the inventor are lost to the
public while magic shadow projection
spreads throughout Europe.

As WITH MANY another inventor, Kircher received little praise and much blame for his invention of the magic lantern. Charges of being in league with the devil to achieve the wondrous images on the screen almost broke his spirit. Though his device was widely pirated in Europe without acknowledgement of the inventor, before Kircher's death he was able to take some satisfaction from the fact that his projector was no longer viewed as "black magic" but as a great boon for mankind. Had he lived longer he would have again been saddened as others claimed the magic lantern as their own. At this later day the name of Kircher was known only to a few scholars although the magic lantern audiences could be numbered in the many thousands.

In the first half century after the invention of the magic lantern projector, four men, in addition to Kircher himself, made its scientific principles and construction widely known. They were a curious group: Gaspar Schott, a protégé of Kircher; Claude Milliet de Chales, a French priest and military expert; Johann Zahn German writer; and William Molyneux, an Irish patriot, teacher and scientist.

Gaspar Schott was the best known of Kircher's pupils who helped to awaken scientific interest in Europe. He was born at

Königshofen, Bohemia, in 1608. He entered the Jesuit Order at the age of 19. Like Kircher, his senior by six years, Schott was compelled to flee the disorders in Germany and continue his studies abroad. For his courses in philosophy and theology Schott went to Sicily. Later he studied under Kircher at the Roman College. From his contact with Kircher, Schott had developed a great interest in scientific matters and mathematics. He conducted research and wrote at Augsburg until his death in 1666. Schott's books were once very popular. Their subjects ranged from extracts of the diaries kept by Kircher on his various scientific travels to mathematical text books and even a study on the source of the river Nile. So far as the story of magic shadows goes, Schott's most valuable book was the *Magia Universalis Naturae et Artis.* "Wonders of Universal Nature and Art," published at Würzburg in 1658, with a second edition in 1674.

Schott described every type of magic lantern, basing his remarks, of course, on the work of Kircher. The projection apparatus described by him was better than that of the master, Kircher. Schott described lanterns with and without lenses, and covered points of practical use as well as the theory.

The age-old Burning Glasses of Archimedes were studied by Schott, who knew about the various kinds of images, mirrors, and the focal length and its importance in producing sharp pictures on the screen. A refinement in the telescope was also explained.

Schott was probably the first man to write about, and study with the magic lantern, optical illusions caused by a rapidly revolving wheel, including the appearance of distorted figures. It was this same study, carried on almost two hundred years later in England, France and Belgium, that was to result in the first real motion pictures. In ideas Schott outran the limitations of the physical apparatus available at the time, as did Kircher himself.

Kircher had been asked by Schott to write the foreword to his book. But Kircher was too busy with other works. (It is barely possible that he was jealous of the growing fame of his former pupil; or, more likely, that he was unwilling to appear in print at that time on the subject which had so much contributed to his troubles.) Nicholas Mohr, who did write the introduction, pointed out that Schott had been carrying on the work of Kircher.

Schott discussed the various details of the magic lantern projector in scientific terms. He was a pure scientist without the dash of showmanship which at once distinguished Kircher and probably helped to cause him difficulty with his "enemies." Schott described how "to construct the Kircher Catoptric Machine." This was the first coupling of Kircher's own name with the magic lantern. But people preferred Kircher's appellation of "magic lantern." And so his own name did not grow into the language to stand for the device he invented.

About fifteen years after Schott's book appeared and nearly thirty years after the first description of the magic lantern by Kircher in his *Great Art of Light and Shadow,* the first prominent Frenchman in the history of the magic shadows made a contribution by improving some details of the projector.

In keeping with what has not been an infrequent practice amongst French historians in claiming inventions for Frenchmen, it has been held that Claude François Milliet de Chales, and not Athanasius Kircher, invented the magic lantern. Milliet de Chales was a talented man but, as he himself clearly wrote, he did not invent the magic lantern. What happened was that de Chales saw one exhibited in Lyons, where he was stationed, and then devised some improvements.

De Chales was much too young to have invented the magic lantern, as he was born at Chambéry in 1621. He entered the Jesuits in 1636 and after his studies spent some time in missionary work in Turkey. While de Chales was on the missions, Kircher had already demonstrated the magic lantern at Rome.

Father de Chales had an interesting career. Upon his return from missionary work he became a professor of humanities and rhetoric. Later his attention was turned to things scientific. Louis XIV made him professor of hydrography at Marseilles and there de Chales was able to devote much time to navigation and to other arts which would have a military application. De Chales later taught mathematics and theology, eventually becoming rector of Chambéry. He died in Turin in 1678.

De Chales' monumental work is *Cursus seu Mundus Mathematicus,* "The Mathematical World," written in 1674. An edition, edited from the author's reviewed manuscript, by Amati Varcin, S. J., was published at Lyons in 1690, 12 years after de Chales' death. One section was devoted to optics. De Chales studied the eye and knew that the image is upside down on the retina. He investigated other vision problems, including angular vision and

Oculus Artificialis Teledioptricus, 1685

JOHANN ZAHN, Gaspar Schott, Claude Milliet de Chales and William Molyneux perfected Kircher's magic lantern projector and spread knowledge of it throughout Europe. Illustrated are table models by Zahn. The mounting of the slides shows the quest for movement. No basic improvements in the projector were made for another century and a half.

Oculus Artificialis Teledioptricus, 1685

Time and wind indicators by projection were among the curious adaptations of the magic lantern device developed by Zahn. Above, the hour was indicated by the point of the sword. Below, the wind instrument was ingeniously connected to a vane on the roof. It was automatic in action; the "clock" was not.

vision at long range, considered binocular vision and the images formed by each eye. He devised satisfactory lenses and spectacles for both far and near-sighted persons. (The original name for near-sightedness—"Myopia"—came down from Aristotle.) De Chales experimented with light and dark colored objects and gave consideration to why we see better with two eyes than one. He noted that the eye actually sees color and light and not objects and movement—a fact upon which the whole motion picture process is based. He pointed out that the ship appears to stand still and the shore moves to an observer aboard. He also studied the nature of color and the laws of light. De Chales even attempted three dimension projection! Even now many efforts are being made to achieve "three dimension" motion pictures without the use of special glasses or other viewing devices for the spectators.

De Chales considered plane and curved mirrors, improving the design of the old *camera lucida* of Alberti by introducing a mirror. He devised a simple searchlight to improve the projection of images, in a system similar to Kircher's design for the first magic lantern, but as it had a stronger light source it was shown how letters, bright enough to read, could be projected a great distance.

De Chales narrated how fires could be set with the two lens system—as the old Burning Glasses of Archimedes. He was a practical man as well as an ingenious one and included details on how to make lenses. Other studies included consideration of color reflection, a telescope with two convex lenses, an attempt to make binoculars and even an experiment with prisms, laying some of the groundwork for Newton.

De Chales wrote that for many things this method of projection —direct with a strong light source—was "the best and most certain." Doubtless he was right, considering available means. He also pointed out the military uses of the projector and other mirror-lens devices. Today in enemy waters or where hostile sea or aircraft are expected and a "radio silence" must be maintained— ships and planes must use optical signaling devices and de Chales was the first to consider carefully this subject.

De Chales' most important refinement in the projector was the introduction of a two-lens projection system.

He described in his book how the magic lantern first came to his attention. "We have seen here at Lyons a dioptric machine, called a magic lantern. Rays of light are projected through a tube for a distance of ten or twelve feet. An enlarged image, about four feet in diameter, is shown in all its colors." The effect was considered wonderful, according to de Chales. He noted, however, that a convex lens was used but pointed out that it would be better to use a double lens "as he demonstrated." De Chales did not discard the concave mirror, used as the light collector on almost all types of projectors from Kircher's to those of the present day.

In a subsequent chapter de Chales gave more information on this subject. "As I have indicated in the preceding chapter a learned Dane" (very likely the same Walgenstein of whom Kircher wrote as a popularizer of his lantern projector) "came to Lyons in the year 1655." De Chales continued, "This Dane was well versed in optics and among other things showed a lantern." De Chales again noted how he had developed an improvement, using two lenses, which made possible a projection to the then amazing distance of 20 feet. The present projection "throw" at the Radio City Music Hall, Rockefeller Center, New York, is approximately 200 feet.

In addition to optics and many other fields of study, de Chales was interested in navigation. He wrote a book, probably on the order of the King's general staff, *The Art of Navigation demonstrated by principle and proved by many observations drawn from practical experience.* He devised a paddle-wheel ship that would go against the current, "without sails, without oars and without the traction of any animal"—surely a military weapon! His most important military work was *The Art of Fortifying and Defending and Attacking according to the French, Dutch, Italian and Spanish Methods.*

De Chales mentioned in his writings Alhazen, Witelo and other ancient authorities. He must have read the first edition of Kircher's book and also Gaspar Schott's before his own was written. However, de Chales made a definite improvement with his lens system which is essentially the modern one. Also, his work helped to popularize and extend the art and science of light and shadow. He was another strange man in this complex story—a missionary, a teacher and a military expert.

Johann Zahn in *Oculus Artificialis Teledioptricus sive Telescopium,* "The Artificial Telescopic Eye or Telescope," published at Nuremberg in 1685 and 1702, outlined a better lens system for the magic lantern and described many applications, including false representations to create wonder and fear. One of Zahn's teachers was Jerome Langenmantel, the editor of Kircher's autobiography, so the link with Kircher is close and direct.

Zahn considered the eye, vision and light, basing his work on earlier writers. It was noted that Kircher, and his aide Schemer, used a system—probably the natural camera—to observe the sun at Rome in 1635. He also described telescopes and microscopes and a device which was a forerunner in the Stereoscope.

In his section on the magic lantern, Zahn acknowledges his debt to Kircher, referring to Kircher's book and to Schott's saying "the projection of images of objects was announced in a wonderful manner by Kircher." He also knew de Chales' work. But he showed that an improvement could be made.

Zahn showed a complete magic lantern, or Thaumaturga Lantern (names originated by Kircher) or Megalographica Lantern (Great-writing), because even little figures and images can appear life-like in size. The system was complete: reflecting mirror to focus the light, a lamp as the light source and two projection lenses forming the projection system.

Zahn wrote, "Very great wonders are presented and set forth in the magic lantern including the projection of light and curious images." He proves himself a showman by saying the purpose is to create "the greatest admiration and enjoyment of those looking on."

The regular magic lantern was, he said, "already well known." He developed some very ingenious improvements, including table model projectors which set the pattern right to the end of the 19th century. All that was later added was improved light sources including, finally, electric light. (Illustrations facing page 64.)

Zahn for his theatre shows described how images could be projected even under water. He stressed the importance of concealing the projector in a separate room so that the audience would not know the source of the magical vision.

In one model of the magic lantern Zahn explained how the glass slides could be mounted on a circular disk which could be revolved in front of the magic lantern lens. In other words, he took the disk shown by Kircher and combined it with Kircher's projector. But Zahn's modification was the dominant pattern used by later experimenters, just before the dawn of the motion picture as we know it. The first projector to show "motion pictures" from hand-drawn slides was invented about 1851 by Franz von Uchatius and looked very similar to this model of Zahn.

Zahn had also many curious applications, including the use of the magic lantern to tell time or rather to project the correct time on a great "clock" on the wall. Another application was the use of the lantern, connected with a wind vane atop the structure to show the direction the wind was blowing at the particular instant. (Illustration facing page 65.)

J. Kunckelius, who wrote on the *Glass Art,* is credited by Zahn with developing a good ink or paint to be used on the glass for the magic lantern slides. This information was passed on by him to his readers. From Kircher's day until the invention of film and its use in photography in the latter part of the 19th century, glass slides formed the physical picture supports for practically every kind of a magic shadow show.

Kircher's magic lantern was established on a scientific basis in the English-speaking world by the writing of William Molyneux, a citizen of Dublin. Molyneux became an Irish patriot by taking a stand against the contended right of the English Parliament to rule Irishmen. He was a leader in the constitutional struggle for Irish autonomy in the early part of the 18th century.

Molyneux, a professor at Trinity College, Dublin, included his treatment of the magic lantern in his *Dioptrica Nova,* which the censor passed on June 4, 1690 with the note, "I think this book is fit to be printed." But it was not published until two years later. Molyneux, as other pioneers in this art-science, had his period of exile. He wrote in *Dioptrica Nova,* "the present distractions of our miserable country have separated me and my books."

In the introduction Molyneux pointed out that up to then there was nothing written in the English language on that part of mathematics and, he said, "I am sure there are many ingenious Heads, great Geometers, and Masters in Mathematics, who are not so well skilled in Latin." And certainly Molyneux was right, for the use of the modern languages was expanding constantly in that period.

Molyneux had a low regard for Zahn, whom he called "a blind transcriber from others" and asserted that he copied the errors of de Chales.

An early section of the book was "On the Representation of outward objects in a Dark Chamber; by a Convex Glass." This was

a modified version of the natural camera, first set down carefully
by da Vinci and dating back to Roger Bacon.

Molyneux devoted a whole section to "The Explication of the
Magick Lantern, sometimes called Lanterna Megalographica"
(that last was one of the names Kircher gave to it). Molyneux
scientifically described a good model featuring a metal lantern and
adjustable lenses. He explained that the pictures to be shown were
painted with transparent colors on pieces of thin glass which were
inverted and placed in the projector. His comment on the type of
picture is entertaining: "This is usually some Ludicrous or fright-
ful Representation, the more to divert the Spectators." "Horror"
pictures—and comedies—were born centuries before Hollywood.

Also discussed were focusing lenses, glass and concave mirrors,
adjustments in the picture focus, the throw from projector to the
screen.

However, Molyneux wished to keep strictly on the scientific
and scholarly side saying, "As to the Mechanick Contrivances of
this Lantern, the most Convenient Proportion of the Glasse, etc.
this is so ordinary amongst the common Glass Grinders that 'tis
needless to insist further thereon in this place. 'Tis sufficient to
me that I have explained the theory thereof."

At the end of the volume there was an advertisement—it was
noted that all the instruments mentioned "are made and sold by
John Yarwell at the Archimedes and Three Golden Prospects,
near the great North Door in St. Paul's Church-Yard: London."
This makes John Yarwell the first recorded commercial dealer in
the magic shadow science.

In addition to Schott, Milliet de Chales, Zahn and Molyneux,
many travelling showmen such as Walgenstein, the Dane, introduced the magic lantern and its magic shadow shows in great
cities and little hamlets of Europe. Some were professional entertainers, accepting the projector as a new device; others were the
"vagabonds and imposters," of the type condemned by Kircher.
This group recognized no law and copied and appropriated the
magic lantern projector whenever opportunity presented itself.
There was no copyright or other protection to restrain them. By the
early part of the 18th Century the magic lantern was common-
place and many men were skilled in its use.

VIII

MUSSCHENBROEK AND MOTION

⌐ Magic shadows move in the projector of Musschenbroek, a Dutchman—Quest for real "motion pictures" continues—Abbé Nollet spins a top—Lantern shows in Paris and London become spectacular.

NOT LONG after Kircher's death his magic lantern projector was in use everywhere in Europe but the apparatus did not do all that was desired. The goal of motion pictures was still around a corner. Pieter van Musschenbroek (1692-1761), a Dutch natural philosopher and mathematician, was the first to successfully simulate motion with the aid of the projector and glass slides.

The effects of motion produced on the screen through the system developed by Musschenbroek were crude but progress was made. There was also further concrete evidence that the primitive urge of the first painter to re-create nature with all its life and movement was still powerful and had not been forgotten.

Previously Zahn, as we have seen, mounted a series of glass slides on a circular disk which could be revolved before the lens of the projector. But there the method really only assured quick changes from one still picture to another. In the very beginning Kircher also had the disk idea and in other models of his lantern arranged the glass slides on a long panel so the successive views could be changed rapidly.

Musschenbroek, working in Holland in the early part of the 18th century, achieved his effect of motion by fitting two panels of slides into the same lantern for simultaneous projection. One slide was stationary and usually depicted the background; the other was mobile and was set in motion by means of a cord. With a skilled manipulator the effects were certainly wonderful—for that period.

The motion magic lantern projector was developed as a hobby by Musschenbroek, who was unaware of its importance until he had a visit in 1736 from the French scientist, or more accurately popularizer of science, Abbé Nollet (1700-1770).

Abbé Nollet corresponded with scientists throughout the world and his salon in Paris was crowded each evening with French and visiting scientists and the hangers-on of the great. While in Holland, Nollet visited Musschenbroek. One evening after a pleasant dinner and much serious conversation on educational and scientific matter, the host, Musschenbroek, proposed a bit of entertainment. He may have told his distinguished French visitor, "I have a surprise for you. I will show you something that is as yet unknown in your wise Paris." It is certain Abbé Nollet's curiosity was stirred up and he looked forward with keen anticipation to the demonstration. He was that kind of a person—eager for any new scientific development or application.

Musschenbroek's show that evening in Holland included, according to Abbé Nollet, magic lantern views of a wind-mill whose arms revolved—wonder of wonders! Also a lady bowing as she walked along the street. And a cavalier removing his hat in courtesy. That would seem to prove that Musschenbroek, the staid scientist, in his idle moments had attempted to create the first "boy-meets-girl" motion picture.

The magic lantern with movement of Musschenbroek's description was brought back to Paris by Nollet who started its popularization. The system became wide-spread following the publication of a book, *Nouvelles Recréations Physiques et Mathématiques,* by Abbé Guyot which went through several editions in Paris and was translated and published also in at least two editions in England by W. Hooper, M.D. under the title, *Rational Recreations in which the Principles of Numbers and Natural Philosophy are Clearly and Copiously Elucidated, by a Series of Easy, Entertaining, Interesting Experiments.* Hooper copied even the plates from the French book of Guyot.

The projections of the magic lantern, it was said, "may be rendered much more amusing, and at the same time more marvelous, by preparing figures to which different natural motions may be given, which everyone may perform according to his own taste; either by movements in the figures themselves, or by painting the subject on two glasses, and passing them at the same time through the groove (of the lantern)." It was noted by Guyot-Hooper that in Musschenbroek's *Philosophical Essays* there are many methods of performing all these movements, "by some mechanical contrivances that are not difficult to execute."

An illustration of the Musschenbroek system was given. The subject sought to portray how, "To represent a tempest by the magic lantern."

> On one of these glasses you are to paint the appearance of the sea, from the slightest agitation to the most violent commotion. Observe that these representations are not to be distinct, but run into each other, that they may form a natural gradation; remember also, that great part of the effect depends on the perfection of the painting, and the picturesque appearance of the design.

> On the other glass you are to paint vessels in different forms and dimensions, and in different directions, together with the appearance of clouds in the tempestuous parts.

Precise instructions were set down for this first "motion picture" storm effect:

> You are then to pass the glass representing the sea slowly through the groove, and when you come to that part where the storm begins, you are to move the glass gently up and down, which will give it the appearance of a sea that begins to be agitated; and so increase the motion till you come to the height of the storm. At the same time you are to introduce the other glass with the ships, and moving in like manner, you will have a natural representation of the sea, and of ships in a calm and in a storm. As you draw the glasses slowly back, the tempest will seem to subside, the sky grow clear, and the ships glide gently over the waves.

With Musschenbroek the magic shadows began to have real motion and the effect on the audience consequently was much greater. Kircher's projector was growing up.

In the Guyot-Hooper book it was also noted, "By means of two glasses disposed in this manner you may represent a battle, or sea fight, and numberless other subjects, that everyone will contrive according to his own taste. They may also be made to represent some remarkable or ludicrous action between different persons, and many other amusements that a lively imagination will easily suggest."

Complete details were given for a "magical theatre" in which regular magic shadow plays could be presented. An elaborate lantern with a number of grooves for slides was proposed. The clouds, palaces of the gods and the like were dropped down from above; the caves and infernal places rose from below; and earthly palaces, gardens, characters, etc. came in from either side—all, of course, on glass slides. Projection was provided by a lamp with a dozen flames. As an illustration a play based on the siege of Troy was suggested. Slides included the following: walls of Troy, the Grecian Camp, the background atmosphere, the Grecian and Trojan troops, ships, the wooden horse, palaces and houses, temple of Pallas, fire and smoke for the conflagration, individual characters, etc. Screen directions were given for a complete magic shadow play in five acts. This surely was among the first—if not the first— motion picture scenario. The screen was then about three feet wide.

Musschenbroek, in addition to being the first credited with introducing effective, though very artificial, motion into light and shadow entertainment and instruction, was said to be the first man to create the illusion of white light by revolving very rapidly a disk painted with seven colors. That effect must have been as magical to Abbé Nollet as his "moving" pictures. It also indicates that considerable advance was being made in the knowledge of vision and the means to create optical illusions, upon which the principle of the motion picture rests.

As many other men in this story, Musschenbroek covered the whole field of science. He studies our old friend, the *camera obscura,* mirrors, prisms, the eye, the microscope in many forms, winds, waterspouts, magnetism, capillary tubes, the size of the earth, sound and pneumatic machines. It is easy to determine from that list of serious studies that Musschenbroek's moving shadow projection was the purest kind of an avocation.

Abbé Nollet who helped to introduce Musschenbroek's novel movement magic lantern is not credited with any great scientific discovery in any field but he served as a clearing house of scientific knowledge in his day. He traveled widely, to Italy and England as well as to Holland.

So far as this tale is concerned, Nollet's name is of significance, after his part in making known the Musschenbroek device, by the fact that he also popularized a very simple little toy—"The Dazzling or Whirling Top."

This little children's plaything helped to stimulate the study of the persistence of vision and led to a better understanding of motion. This in turn resulted, within a half century, in learning a way to re-create actual motion effects. Around 1760 Nollet developed the top which, though only an outline in form, when whirled rapidly appears to be a solid object. Nollet also described the use of the *camera obscura* and the various types of lanterns for entertainment and teaching purposes.

Benjamin Franklin (1706-1790), famed American statesman, writer and scientist, corresponded with Abbé Nollet. Franklin, though disagreeing with Nollet on electricity, admired him, calling him "an able experimenter." Nollet marveled that such science as manifest by the publication of certain of Franklin's works in Paris could come from America. At first he conceived that his enemies in Paris had falsified the papers to cause his embarrassment. Franklin made no direct contribution to the art-science of magic shadows but had a pertinent remark to make about the medium—light itself—which is nearly as true today as when he wrote it in 1752 for a paper read to the Royal Society in London: "I must own I am much in the dark about light," he said.

IX

PHANTASMAGORIA

◡ Magic lanterns mounted on wheels and images projected on screens of smoke make ghost shadow plays—Robertson "resurrects" Louis XVI—Théâtre Robert Houdin, Paris, 1845, Polytechnic Institution, London, 1848 and Nazi Army, 1940—all use magic shadows for supernatural effects.

THE TONGUE-TWISTING word, Phantasmagoria, stands for a certain type of light and shadow show popular immediately after the French Revolution. It marked a definite throwback in the story of magic shadows. It was essentially a revival of the medieval black magic or necromantic use of light and shadow to trick, deceive and keep everyone "in the dark about light."

Phantasmagoria is the magic lantern illusion associated with making phantasms appear before an audience. The only contribution to the art-science is that it created an illusion of motion through the novel means of moving the projector instead of the slides or film.

The Phantasmagoria magic lantern was mounted on rollers and the lens was adjustable so that ghosts would appear to grow and diminish and move about. Certain dissolve effects were also produced. For Phantasmagoria the images—regularly ghosts—were projected not on a screen but on smoke, a factor which naturally contributed to the weird effects.

Phantasmagoria was most popular in Paris in the late 1790s, probably as some kind of a psychological reaction to the horrors

75

of the French Revolution. Men and women of the day thought much of death, ghosts and the like.

The basic idea for combining motion illusions successfully with the magic lantern is traced directly to Musschenbroek. The use of smoke for a screen goes back to the ancient practitioners of light and shadow trickery.

Guyot showed, on a small scale, how ghost illusions can be projected on smoke. He noted, "It is remarkable in this representation, that the motion of smoke does not at all change the figures, which appear so conspicuous that the spectator thinks he can grasp them with his hand."

These devices were intended primarily for simple amusement on a private or semi-private scale.

An indication of the mood of the European people of the time is the fame granted Alessandro Conte di Cagliostro (1743-1795). This man whose real name was Giuseppe Balsamo was known throughout Europe in the latter part of the 18th century. Thomas Carlyle wrote about him under the title "Count Cagliostro." He used all kinds of deceptive devices, and was jailed in France, England and in his native Italy where he died.

The black magic of Cagliostro, the phantasm images, and a third factor, the Shadow Plays, were to be combined to make the Phantasmagoria.

Earlier mention has been made of the Chinese Shadow Plays which have been in use in the Far East for thousands of years. Towards the middle of the 18th century the Shadow Plays were very popular in Germany. Shadows were used to portray action. The audience sat before a translucent screen on which were cast, by means of a strong light source, shadows of the various players or objects. In certain arrangements a regular magic lantern would also be used, projecting, from in front of the screen, the background scenery or cloud and sky effects.

A showman named François Seraphin has been credited with introducing the Shadow Plays—*Ombres Chinoises*—into France in 1772. He got the idea during his travels in Italy. Then the shadow entertainment received its French "first night" at the Palace of Versailles. Light and Shadow Plays were very popular at the royal court, especially with the children. In 1784 Seraphin decided that the entertainment was ready for introduction on a popular basis— the trend of the times may well have influenced his decision.

The Shadow Play theatre of Seraphin was moved from Versailles to the Palais-Royal and its popularity continued for a time. Shadow entertainment was carried on by members of the same family till past the middle of the 19th century when an attempt was made to regain popularity by using marionettes. Other Shadow Plays continued to attract audiences in Paris until the end of the 19th century, when the pre-motion picture devices became popular.

Phantasmagoria reached its peak under an extraordinary character—Etienne Gaspard Robert (1763-1837), a Belgian and a practicer of a multitude of professions and hobbies. Robert, for some reason, called himself Robertson. Robertson started life on a serious enough basis and in time became professor of physics in his native town of Liége.

Robertson tells in his memoirs how he came upon the works of Kircher, Schott and many others, who, he believed, practiced magic. He read up on optics and, about 1784, exhibited in Holland, where he was at the time, an improved magic lantern. He was greatly influenced by the results of Musschenbroek and the success of the Shadow Plays at Versailles. Robertson's characters were ghosts. He commented, "the encouragements that I received made me try to improve my methods." More and more persons were attracted to Robertson's shows in Holland and finally even the burgomaster attended.

At Paris Robertson improved his knowledge of the magic lantern. There he met Jacques Alexandre César Charles, who was using a lantern for scientific purposes at his laboratory in the Louvre. Robertson sought a brighter light source for the lantern and persisted in his quest even though Charles was said to have tried to discourage him by pointing out that much money had been spent in vain on that project.

At the time of the Revolution, Robertson laid before the Government a plan which would authorize him to build a huge burning mirror, as Archimedes did, so that he could destroy any attacking English fleet before it could reach the "invasion coast." No action was taken on the proposal. In our own day the English were ready to burn any Nazi invasion fleet which sailed from France—not by burning glasses but by equally amazing devices.

After the Revolution, during the stormy days of the first French Republic, Robertson held "seances" at the Pavillion de l'Echiquier. A projector mounted on wheels was used. A patent on the device under the name of Fantascope or Phantoscope was obtained on March 29, 1799.

Robertson's characters or ghosts which would appear to grow and disappear on the screen of smoke were usually such heroes as Voltaire, Rousseau, Marat, and Lavoisier. At the end of each performance, a skeleton would appear and Robertson would remark that this was the fate awaiting each one in the audience. Grim entertainment!

A clever artist, Robertson had a large collection of slides and would call upon his audience—which never quite knew whether to believe that he was in league with the devil and brought the ghosts into appearance or not—to ask for whichever ghost they wished. You can imagine the effect when some Frenchman called for Marat and then, small at first and gradually growing large until life-size and more, a shadowy, recognizable image of Marat would appear.

This "request" part of the program caused Robertson trouble. One night, a member of the audience who had had a few extra sips of wine, or who was terrified beyond the others, called for the return of the ghost of Louis XVI. This was too much. The authorities shut the theatre and refused to grant Robertson permission to continue his "seances." They did not want even the ghost of Louis returned. Political censorship of screen entertainment had made its first appearance.

Robertson went to Bordeaux to make sure that he, himself, did not prematurely join Louis and his other ghosts.

Later he was able to return to Paris and open another theatre near the Place Vendôme. This was a particularly startling auditorium. He used an abandoned chapel of a Capuchin monastery. Robertson's light and shadow ghosts came to life among the mortal remains of ancient monks. (The reader may be aware of the ancient Capuchin custom of using bones of deceased members of the order as part of the ornament of their chapels as a constant reminder of death.)

Even though Robertson had admitted that from childhood he had the keenest interest in things marvelous, he tired of his magic. Next we hear of him, he is a pioneer balloonist, credited with the invention of one of the early parachutes! On July 18, 1803, he made a notable ascent in a balloon.

In 1845 there was opened in Paris a theatre which was to play a part in the light and shadow story. It was called for its proprietor and chief performer, Théâtre Robert Houdin. Houdin, after whom Harry Houdini of the 20th century named himself, practiced every kind of trick and wondrous illusion. He used Phantasmagorial effects and the French public flocked to the shows. Towards the end of the century Emile Reynaud took over the Théâtre Robert Houdin and showed the best magic shadow plays prior to the introduction of the motion picture itself.

During the middle of the century, the Polytechnic Institution, at London, attracted large crowds with magic lantern shows. Ghosts were created à la Robertson and the Phantasmagorial methods. Regular entertainment was also provided with such magic lantern stories as *Puss in Boots* and versions of Swift's *Gulliver's Travels* and *The Tale of the Tub*. As many as a half-dozen magic lanterns would be used to create impressive scenes, such as battles.

In our own day attempts have been made to use Phantasmagorial effects to frighten and deceive. An interesting example is contained in the following Associated Press dispatch telling how the Nazis attempted to make the English soldiers believe that Heaven was entreating them to abandon the war:

Paris, Feb. 15 (1940) (AP)—Press accounts from the front sector occupied by the British reported today that Tommies manning an outpost during the night suddenly saw an image of the Virgin Mary appear in the clouds, with her arms outstretched in entreaty.

The commander sent out a patrol, which returned with the information that the Germans were projecting the image from a machine on the ground.

Phantasmagoria is not dead yet. Television may even increase the possibilities of this type of magic shadow diversion.

X

DR. PARIS' TOY

An English physician, Dr. Paris, invents the Thaumatrope, a simple device which creates the illusion of motion by having one part of a picture on one side of a disk and the other on the reverse side—Scientific instrument and child's plaything.

DURING THE period which followed the defeat of Napoleon at Waterloo, there appeared, first in London and later in Paris and elsewhere, a small cardboard toy which was at once the plaything of children and a scientific curiosity which illustrated in a startling way the illusion of the persistence of vision. This toy was the Thaumatrope.

The name Thaumatrope means "wonder-turner" (a word reminiscent of one of Kircher's titles for the magic shadow projection art —*thaumaturga*). The Thaumatrope is a small disk with one image on the face and another on the back. Two short threads or bits of string are attached to the disk. The Thaumatrope's effects are observed by twirling the disk. The eye, as in the case of motion pictures, does not distinguish the separate pictures on each side of the disk but only the one, combined impression.

A variation of the Thaumatrope, however, came even closer to the motion picture idea—the two ends of cord were not set opposite each other, which resulted in an irregular motion and an additional illusion.

John Ayrton Paris (1785-1856), an English doctor, has the best claim to the invention of the Thaumatrope. At any rate, he was responsible for the popularity of this scientific toy. Paris was a skilled physician who was specially known for his talent in judging the health of his patients by their general appearance. He took interest in affairs well outside his medical profession and was respected as a conversationalist whose talk enlivened many a drawing room evening in London. A keen mind and a great memory, even for the smallest detail, were qualities that helped to make Paris a charming companion.

For recreation Paris wrote a "novel" called, *Philosophy in Sport Made Science in Earnest; being an attempt to illustrate the first principles of natural philosophy by aid of Popular Toys and Sports.* The work was published in three small volumes, in keeping with the 19th century custom that every novel must be issued in three volumes. Paris used a thread of story as a frame-work on which to build the various scientific illustrations. The book *Philosophy in Sport,* shows the influence of the novelist-humorist Thomas Love Peacock. It was dedicated to the novelist, Maria Edgeworth.

Paris' work was published anonymously in 1827 and was a "best seller" all through the rest of his life. On his death-bed in 1856 he was busy revising the proofs of the 8th edition.

The first part of the third volume dealt with the Thaumatrope which Paris informed his readers could be obtained "at Mr. William Phillip's, George Yard, Lombard Street, the publisher." Paris continued, "We mention this circumstance to guard the reader against those inferior imitations which are vended in the shops of London." George Cruikshank, 1792-1878, the skilled illustrator, who worked on books of Scott and Dickens, made some of the designs for Paris' Thaumatrope.

Paris introduced the Thaumatrope amid a great number of puns which perhaps were very funny in his day.

No sooner had Mr. Seymour put the card in motion than the vicar, in a tone of the greatest surprise, exclaimed, "Magic! Magic! I declare the rat is in the cage!!"

"And what is the motto?" asked Louisa.

"Why is this rat like an opposition member in the House of Commons, who joins the ministry?" replied Mr. Seymour.

"Ha, ha, ha—excellent," cried the major, as he read the following answer: "because by *turning round* he gains a snug berth, but ceases to be free."

*

"Show us another card," said Tom, eagerly.

"Here then is a watch-box; when I turn it round, you will see the watchman comfortably sleeping at his post."

"Very good! It is very surprising," observed the vicar.

"Yes," observed the major; "and to carry on your political joke, it may be said that, like most worthies who gain a post, by turning round, he sleeps over his duty."

One epigram, accompanying a Thaumattope card, had a reference to the recent activities of Napoleon:

Head, legs and arms, alone appear;
Observe that nobody is here:
Napoleon-like I undertake
Of nobody a king to make.

Paris, as inventor of the Thaumatrope, could not avoid the temptation to have a little speech from the anonymous inventor, himself: "The inventor confidently anticipates the favour and patronage of an enlightened and liberal public, on the well-grounded assurance that 'one good turn deserves another'; and he trusts that his discovery may afford the happy means of giving activity to wit that has been long stationary; of revolutionizing the present system of standing jokes, and of putting into rapid circulation the most appreciated *bon mots*."

The Thaumatrope was advertised in the following way:

The Thaumatrope

being

Rounds of Amusement

or

How to Please and Surprise

by turns.

Through the characters of his "novel," Paris then commented on the illusion of the persistence of vision which makes the Thaumatrope (and the motion picture) a reality. He discussed the whirling flame which appeared to make a circle; Homer's reference to "long shadowed" spear; and the tail of a rocket.

Paris also described an improved model of the Thaumatrope. In this card device a center disk is allowed to change from one position to another as the whole revolves. In one illustration a jockey was on one side and a horse on the other. By tightening the strings as the card revolved the jockey appeared to be falling over the neck of the horse. In another an Indian juggler was represented as using two, then three and finally four balls. Other illusions indicated were a sailor rowing a boat, "a dandy making a bow." Through the words of the vicar, Paris then warned, "I hope that, amidst all your improvements (in the Thaumatrope), you will still keep in view your first and most laudable design, that of rendering it subservient to classical illustration."

It is certain that Paris developed the Thaumatrope, first, for scientific illustration of the persistence of vision, perhaps to better explain the phenomenon to one of his patients or students. But being a clever man, he immediately realized its commercial value and arranged to have sets of the cards made up and sold in London. Doubtless the chapter in his book on the Thaumatrope did much to increase the sale of the toys.

David Brewster (1781-1868), Scottish scientist whose work on the polarization of light led him to invent, around 1815, the Kaleidoscope—an optical instrument which creates and exhibits by reflection a variety of beautiful symmetrical designs in varied colors—was the first to comment in print on the Thaumatrope of Paris, the year before the latter's book appeared. In the fourth volume of his *Edinburgh Journal* Brewster wrote, under the description of the Thaumatrope, "a very ingenious philosophical toy, invented, we believe, by Dr. Paris." Brewster remarked that the circular disks should be 2½ inches in diameter and that the cord should be of silk. Brewster described the following Thaumatrope cards: Rose-tree and garden-pot, horse and man, a branch with and without leaves, woman in one dress and then another, body of a Turk and his head, watchman's box and the watchman, Harlequin and Columbine, comic head and wig, a man asleep and awake, and the use of the cards for cipher writing. According to Brewster, "the principle of the thaumatrope may be extended to many other devices." He also commented on the imperfections of the toy arising from the hobbling effect of irregular rotation. He suggested that a "solid axis of rotation is decidedly preferable and will produce much more pleasing combinations."

Brewster himself was deeply interested in light and vision phenomena. Despite its original scientific purposes, his Kaleidoscope also was a popular toy. Brewster patented the toy in 1816 but it was pirated. Some 200,000 were sold in three months. In his *Treatise on the Kaleidoscope,* 1819, Brewster told it was discovered while he was testing the successive reflections of gold and silver plates. He also noted the application of the Kaleidoscope to Kircher's magic lantern in order to bring the effects before a large audience at one time.

The invention of the Thaumatrope has been attributed to others besides Paris, despite the weighty authority of Brewster and Paris' own book. Charles Babbage (1792-1871), English scientist and mathematician noted for his calculating machine and his campaign against noise (which he said robbed us of one-quarter of our working life), attributed the discovery of the Thaumatrope to his friend and classmate, John Herschel, the astronomer, (1792-1871). Babbage wrote in his autobiography that one evening Herschel spun a shilling before a mirror so that both sides of it could be visible—the Thaumatrope effect. Dr. William Fitton, Captain Kaster and Dr. William Hyde Wollaston (1766-1828) were told about the method and various Thaumatropes were made, according to Babbage, about 1818 or 1819. "After a lapse of some time the device was forgotten. Then in 1826," Babbage wrote "during a dinner at the Royal Society Club, Sir Joseph Banks being in the chair, I heard Mr. Barrow, then Secretary to the Admiralty, talking very loudly about a wonderful invention of Dr. Paris, the object of which I could not quite understand." Babbage then claimed it was his invention. At any rate, Paris and not Herschel, Fitton, Wollaston or Babbage, was the one to popularize the Thaumatrope.

In passing, it may be noted that at the time Paris was making the Thaumatrope well known Babbage was thinking about submarine craft: "Such a vessel" (a four-man submarine equipped for a 48-hour stay under water) "could be propelled by a screw and might enter, without being suspected, any harbour, and place any amount of explosive matter under the bottoms of ships."

XI

PLATEAU CREATES MOTION PICTURES

⸎Plateau, blind half of his life, develops devices to show motion from hand-drawn images, opening the road to the modern motion picture—Stampfer independently invents similar apparatus—Persistence of vision studied.

PLATEAU, A BELGIAN scientist who became blind in work that resulted in making it possible for millions all over the world to see motion pictures, deserves more than anyone else the title, "Father of the Motion Picture." Just as Athanasius Kircher originated projection as we know it with the magic lantern, Joseph Antoine Ferdinand Plateau has the best claim of all to credit for making the motion picture illusion a reality.

Never interested in profits for himself, Plateau did not trouble to patent his magic disk picture machines but took pains to issue correct instructions when commercial imitators made devices lacking in some essential.

Plateau was born on Oct. 14, 1801, at Brussels, Belgium, the son of a landscape and flower painter. His mother was the former Catherine Thirion. From earliest boyhood, Plateau was trained to be an artist and the nature of his studies and work in later life indicated that he must have shown great promise, for he had the temperamental qualities of a great artist. After his elementary studies, his father lost no time in directing his son's attention towards the arts by sending him to the Academy of Design at Brussels.

At the age of 14 Plateau was left an orphan, and was made a

ward of his maternal uncle. In delicate health young Plateau was sent into the country to recuperate from the shock of losing both his parents in two years. The location selected was near Waterloo and Plateau had to take shelter in the woods for ten days and nights while the battle raged. Soon the plans Plateau's father had made for him to study art were altered. The uncle was a lawyer and wished his ward to succeed him in that profession. Plateau himself evidently was strong-willed and persevering even at an early age, for during the next few years he studied both arts and sciences. This would make it possible for him to follow his father's, his uncle's, or his own wish. He wanted to strike out into a new field, and this he did.

Higher studies were carried on at the Royal College and in 1822, at the age of 21, Plateau entered the University of Liége as a candidate for a degree both in philosophy and letters, and in science. As the years progressed Plateau turned more and more of his attention toward science, especially problems concerning color, vision and the perception of motion. But all through life he retained the fullness of viewpoint of a man with a background and interests in many fields so his imagination never was dulled, as sometimes happens in the cases of specialists in a restricted field of science. The art of his father never left him.

While studying for the doctorate Plateau carried on his first important work in vision and motion which resulted in the scientific approach to the first motion picture machine. He investigated the visual effects of whirling a disk which was colored half in yellow, half in blue.

In 1827 part of Plateau's research was published in Quetelet's *Correspondance Mathématique et Physique*. Quetelet (1796-1874) was a pioneer in statistics and Plateau's professor at the Royal College, and also taught at the Museum of Science and Letters in Belgium. The next year, 1828, Plateau sent another communication to M. Quetelet on the appearances produced by two lines turning around a point with uniform motion. In that letter Plateau referred to the work of Roget on persistence of vision published in the *Philosophical Transactions* of the Royal Society, London, 1824.

Peter Mark Roget (1779-1869), English doctor best known for his *Thesaurus of English Words and Phrases,* combined his medical work with interest in the sciences. On December 9, 1824, he read, at the Royal Society, a paper called, "Explanation of an optical deception in the appearance of the spokes of a wheel seen through vertical apertures." Roget pointed out that the phenomenon had been noted but not explained by an anonymous contributor who signed himself "J. M." in the *Quarterly Journal* of December 1, 1820. "J. M." commented on the curvature of spokes when a wheel is in motion and is viewed through a series of vertical bars. Everyone has noted the strange rotations of motor car wheels when viewed under certain conditions, as in the modern motion picture. "J. M." pointed out that at times the wheel appeared to rotate backwards; at other times, forward and still again seem to stand still. A nod of praise should be bestowed towards "J. M." (these are not the initials of any of the better known English scientists of the period). Ten years later the great Faraday confessed he did not know the identity of this man who had stimulated those investigations which we now know led directly to the first actual motion pictures formed from hand-drawn designs.

Roget, in 1824, noted that a certain velocity and a certain amount of light were necessary before the "wheel phenomenon" was visible—both speed of motion and bright light source are necessary for the motion picture illusion. Roget said, "It is evident from the facts above stated that the deception in the appearance of the spokes must arise from the circumstances of separate parts only of each spoke being seen at the same moment; the remaining parts being concealed from view by the bars" (equivalent to the shutters in the motion picture machine). Roget continued, "so that it is evident that the several portions of one and the same line, seen through the intervals of the bars, form on the retina the images of so many different radii." Roget remarked that the illusion was the same as when a bright object is whirled in a circle—"an impression made by a pencil of rays on the retina, if sufficiently vivid, will remain for a certain time after the cause has ceased."

A few weeks later, on December 24, 1824, Roget lectured on the persistence of vision with regard to moving objects, a phenomenon first recognized by the ancient scientists.

Plateau wrote in 1828 as follows:

I have made an instrument by means of which I could produce these fixed images with ease and I also could make visible the formation of changes in the curvature . . . when working at my first experiments relative to sensations, I observed that while turning rapidly a wheel whose teeth were perpendicular to its axis, and placing the eye at some distance from the plane of the axis, one perceived the image of a series of perfectly immobile teeth; that also with two wheels revolving, the one behind the other, with considerable speed and in opposite directions, produced in the eye the sensation of a fixed wheel. I have remarked further that, while the two wheels are not concentric, the fixed image appears to be made up of curved lines.

Today stroboscopic machines, based on the principles of Plateau's devices, are used to study moving objects. In this way modern scientists learn more about the nature of movement and its stresses on wheels and other objects.

Plateau received the degree of doctor of physical and mathematical sciences from the University of Liége on June 3, 1829, when he was 28. His thesis was on "Certain Properties of the Impressions Produced by Light upon the Organ of Sight." It is strange that such a learned paper would have so much influence on what was to be the modern motion picture.

The chief points—all of importance in building motion pictures —of the Plateau thesis dated April 24, 1829, were: First, the sensation (result of the picture presented to the eye) must stay for a time to form completely—this hinted definitely at the necessity of intermittent movement for a really successful and practical motion picture machine. Second, the sensations do not disappear immediately but gradually dim—this makes motion pictures possible. If each image disappeared all at once, only individual still pictures would be recognized. The gradually dimming makes possible fusion of one image with the next which results in appearance of motion. The third point covered was the relative effect on the eye of various colors. Plateau concluded that the intensity of the chief colors decreased from white, yellow, red, blue —in that order. He also announced results of perception of various colors at different angles, studies made in the shade and in the light. It was further pointed out that two colors—as two images— changed rapidly result in only one sensation or image.

After receiving his doctor's degree from the University, Plateau taught at the Royal College of Liége while he continued his research on vision and related matters.

*JOSEPH PLATEAU sacrificed his own eyesight in
an effort to enable others to see pictures in motion.*

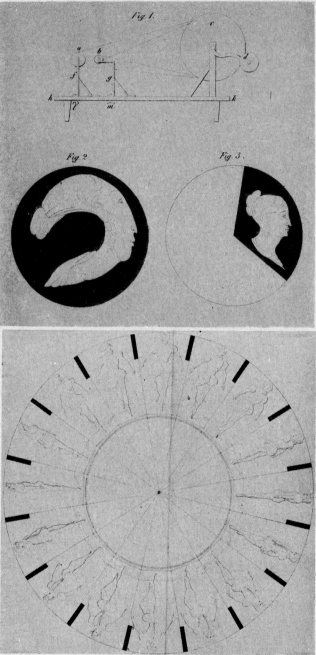

Correspondance Mathématique, 1829-1833

PLATEAU'S *first real motion picture device,
shown above, see page 89. Below, the Phénakisticope with which a single person could see
pictures in motion.*

The first machine creating the illusion of motion from a series of drawings was described by Plateau in a letter to Quetelet dated Liége, December 5, 1829, with the scientific title, "Different Optical Experiments." (*Relative à différentes expériences d'optique.*) A similar instrument was already referred to by Plateau in his paper written in the preceding year. Although the device made by Plateau in 1828 and described in the 1829 article followed by several years the introduction of the Thaumatrope, it rates as the first motion picture machine because the Thaumatrope was really only a scientific toy, just as Paris called it.

Plateau illustrated his letter describing his instrument in writing to Quetelet in answer to an inquiry. The drawing (opposite page) of Plateau shows that, though a scientist, he never forgot his early training and was something of an artist. The principles of his machine could be illustrated by drawings of lines and other geometrical figures, but Plateau chose a woman's head.

In the following words Plateau described his instrument:

Two small copper pulleys, (a) and (b), drive by means of an endless cord a large wooden wheel, (c), which has a double groove; the diameters of the small pulleys are such that the two cords are equally taut and the system is placed in movement by means of the handle, (d), the speed of one pulley being an exact multiple of the other; the axes terminate in the form of a vise and are divised in such a way that you can attach to them by little screws the drawings or cartoons with which you wish to experiment. The pulleys are held by iron supports, (f) and (g), which slide in two grooves practically parallel with the stand or base (hk), and are held in position by means of thumb screws.

Lines or drawings to be studied are mounted on the two pulleys. The machine is of such a nature, Plateau pointed out, that drawings can be easily changed, the relative speeds of the two wheels (one serving as a shutter when drawings are used) can be regulated, alignment can be readjusted and by crossing the cords the disks can be made to rotate in opposite directions.

Plateau continued by explaining that when the speed on one disk is not an exact multiple of the other they do not keep the same relative positions after rotation.

A different image is produced at each revolution and the eye, instead of seeing one fixed line (or image), sees only a rapid succession of different lines (or images); however if the swifter is little more than a multiple of the other, the difference is very little in a manner which the eye cannot distinguish one from another. In this case the spectacle will appear to change little by little. . . .

There is the germ of the motion picture—a real instrument which makes pictures move.

The diagram illustrates a model in which "a perfectly regular image is produced from a deformed figure" turning in a speed proportional to the distortion behind the shutter disk.

Plateau pointed out that the deformed figure can be painted black and turn before a white surface, or be white and turn behind a slot pierced in a black disk. He said, "This last method is preferable to the other because it gives an image of greater lifelikeness . . . ." This of course is the quality sought in all dramatic representations—realistic living pictures.

"For this effect," he explained, "you design the deformed figure on white transparent paper and paint the surrounding space with a very opaque black, then make the experiment carefully, and place a strong light behind the paper."

In the example shown in the drawing the two disks, mounted one behind the other, are rotated in an opposite direction, the motion of the deformed figure is double that of the shutter and the effect produced is that of the regular image shown in Figure 3.

Plateau then remarked, "The construction of these images is very simple." He gave the method and an example. "While the shutter will be making a third part of a revolution all the points of the circle carrying the deformed figure will be present behind it and in consequence it will produce one regular complete image. Then during the second and third part of the revolution of the shutter it will be able to form itself into second and third images resembling the first." These were the words Plateau used to explain the nature of the operations of the first movie machine.

He concluded: "As you are master of the production of the figures you can make them as bizarre and as irregular as you wish." Producers of the modern motion picture have indeed made pictures that are both "bizarre" and "irregular." Plateau would have liked modern motion pictures because he was fond of the theatre, especially liking comedies.

While Plateau was making the experiments in 1829 which led to scientific presentations of visual and optical phenomena as well as construction of the first motion picture machine to illustrate those principles as well as to entertain, a tragic event happened. Plateau in his investigations of seeing light and motion gave special attention to the chief source of all light on earth, the sun.

One day, to see for himself the effects of a great stimulus, the greatest possible in nature on his eye, he stared at the sun for 25 seconds without glasses or other protection. The intensity was great and the effect equal. He was blind for the rest of that day. In a few days his sight came back but it was permanently injured. It gradually waned and was gone in 1843. A choroid inflammation persisted and blotted out the vision of one of the greatest investigators of vision in all history.

During the period while his sight was gradually going, Plateau continued work on vision and made great contributions to the then unknown motion picture. From 1843 he had to discontinue teaching on account of total blindness but this did not stop his experiments.

In 1830 Plateau published a further explanation of his wheel device in Quetelet's Journal.

In 1831 and 1832 Plateau and Michael Faraday (1791-1867), English scientist, had a written argument over certain phases of priority in observing the "wheel phenomenon" which led to the motion picture. On December 10th, 1830, Faraday, the son of a blacksmith, who attracted the attention of Sir Humphry Davy, addressed the Royal Institution of Great Britain "On the Peculiar Class of Optical Deceptions." The paper was published in February, 1831, in the Institution's *Journal*. Faraday, called by Tyndall, "the greatest experimental philosopher the world has ever seen," was attracted to the wheel phenomenon which he noted "J. M." had discussed in 1820 and Roget in 1824. At the lead mills of Messrs. Maltsby Faraday saw cog wheels rapidly revolving one in one direction, the other in another. The optical effect was curious. He designed in his laboratory a disk machine in order to create the same illusion, noting that the effects produced were sometimes beautiful. Faraday said that the device of the revolving wheels could be spun before a mirror and interesting results observed. He did not propose the use of images or pictures. Mr. Wheatstone, Faraday said, was engaged in the general exploration of the subject and hoped soon that the results would be made public.

Plateau later in the year wrote in the *Annales de Chimie et de Physique,* a scientific publication printed in Paris and edited by Guy-Lussac and Arago, that scientists both in France and England were studying the effects of two revolving wheels, one placed behind the other and each revolving at different speeds.

Plateau claimed priority in these words: "Several years ago I observed those phenomena and from that conducted experiments whose results were published. My experiments attracted little attention outside the country and Mr. Faraday without doubt had no knowledge of my work . . . It is because such a man as Mr. Faraday has decided that the phenomenon in question was not unworthy of his attention that I attach some merit to the honor of having observed it before him."

In the 1832 edition of the *Correspondance Mathématique et Physique* of Quetelet, Plateau remarked (in a note dated January 20, 1833) that following the letter published in the *Annales* of November, 1831, "He (Faraday) wrote me and recognized in a manner most flattering for me the priority of my observations." Plateau finally concluded that Faraday had had some knowledge after all of his earlier work when the Englishman wrote his paper at the end of 1830.

Plateau acknowledged that Faraday's paper had some interesting observations which he explained and enlarged upon. Following the principle outlined in his work of 1828, Plateau then constructed the first Fantascope or Phénakisticope, the first machine which created illusions of motion from a series of pictures. Madou, a brother-in-law of Quetelet, was credited with copying Plateau's drawing with extreme care.

Plateau conceived the idea of having successively different pictures which would give the illusion of motion for use on the revolving disk. With each figure showing some changes of position from the preceding, the illusion is that the figures move and not the disk; and so it is with modern motion pictures. We have no consciousness of the movement of film through the machine before our eyes—only of movement of the figures on the film as projected on the screen. (Illustration facing page 89.)

Plateau also pointed out that a strong light was necessary for the motion pictures—as today—and that the "projector" must be a certain distance from the mirror (now a screen) on which the images are seen.

"I shall not describe the variety of curious illusion which can be produced by this new method," Plateau concluded. "I leave to the imagination of persons who would try these experiences the care to find out the most interesting."

Motion picture producers down to this day, using their imagination, have followed the challenge of Plateau, and still the field is inexhaustible.

In the *Annales de Chimie et de Physique* for 1833 Plateau gave a further explanation of his device, named by others the Phénakisticope. Others had also commercialized it. McLeans' Optical Illusions, No. 26 Haymarket Street, London, and other firms were selling models based on Plateau's invention. "I wish to take this opportunity to state, that while the Phénakisticope has been made from an idea which I have published on this new method of creating illusions, I have no part whatsoever in the execution of this instrument which leaves much to be desired according to reports. The theory and experiments have shown that to obtain results as perfect as possible it is necessary to take certain precautions which have been omitted in the Phénakisticope."

Plateau went on to explain that he had made some models in which the necessary steps had been taken and "these models now constitute a new instrument which has been published in London under the name of Fantascope."

The improved instrument was described with the original dancer and marching men as illustrations. He also pointed out that the disks must revolve at a certain speed—if too slow, the illusion of motion is not present, and if too rapid the figures become blurred.

At about the same time Plateau invented his Phénakisticope or Fantascope independently, the same device was invented by Simon Ritter von Stampfer, an Austrian geometrician and geologist. Stampfer was born October 28, 1792, in the Tyrol. As a young boy he stared at the sun for a long period but recovered his normal sight after the image of the sun persisted for 24 days. When a professor of practical geometry at the Polytechnical Institute at Vienna, Stampfer published his account of the Stroboscope, as he called it, in 1834. Stampfer in his article mentioned Dr. Paris'

Thaumatrope, Dr. Roget's paper on the persistence of vision in regard to wheel spokes and the paper of Faraday—all mentioned above. Stampfer's treatment of the disks to create the illusion of motion was a mathematical one. He explained many complicated mathematical formulae and unlike the Plateau papers his were not accompanied by a drawing. Stampfer, though not having Plateau's artistic talent, was a more practical man. On May 7, 1833, he took out an Imperial patent on his invention. Stampfer died on November 10, 1864, in Vienna.

Plateau himself is the best authority for the respective claims of himself and Stampfer, though as always he may have been much more modest and generous than the facts warranted for basically his disk had much greater influence than Stampfer's and his research was started first.

While describing an improved form of his original Anorthoscope, or machine used to create distorted images developed first in 1828 and 1829, Plateau wrote on the invention of the Phénakisticope, Fantascope or Stroboscope, in 1836 in the *Bulletin* of the Royal Academy of Belgium:

> I would like to take this occasion to say here a few words on the question of my priority to the invention of another instrument, the Fantascope or Phénakisticope, priority which is shared equally with Mr. Stampfer, professor at Vienna, who has published a similar instrument under the name of Stroboscopic Disks.
>
> In the notice which accompanies the second edition of these Stroboscopic Disks printed in July of 1833, Mr. Stampfer stated that he had commenced in December of the preceding year to repeat the experiments of Mr. Faraday on certain illusions of optics and that these experiments had resulted in the invention of the instrument which he had published. Also the editors affirmed in a foreword that in the month of February of the following year Mr. Stampfer had assembled a collection of these disks and had shown them successively to his friends, including prominent persons. They brought it about that on May 7 of that year he was given an exclusive Imperial patent to the rights to his invention.
>
> So much for what concerns Mr. Stampfer. One sees that the patent above mentioned was not obtained until May 7, 1833.

The professor has not been able to place his first publication prior to that time. But, on the other hand, the letter which gives first description of my Fantascope is dated January 20, 1832. Thus my first publication is over a year before that of Mr. Stampfer. As for the time when I first got the idea for this instrument, the idea to which I was also led by the paper of Mr. Faraday, it is difficult for me to be precise; however, the drawing which accompanies that letter proved that I had already at that time finished the first disk and when I recall my labor, the difficulties which I encountered in the first construction and the extreme care which I had given to it, I believe that I can place the invention at about the same time, that is to say, as Mr. Stampfer, in the month of December, 1832.

Roget also may be considered a pioneer in this field. In 1834 he wrote that Faraday's writing had called again to his attention wheel devices and that in the Spring of 1831 he had constructed several "which I showed to many of my friends," he wrote, "but in consequence of occupations and cares of a more serious kind I did not publish any account of this invention which was last year reproduced on the continent."

From 1835 until 1843 Plateau continued his work and teaching at the University of Liége in his capacity of professor of experimental physics, taking time off to be married in 1840 to Fanny Clavareau. But all the while the man who had helped to bring visual education and entertainment to millions who were to come after him was gradually going blind. He was a popular teacher, despite his handicap.

From 1844, when his vision was entirely gone, Plateau worked continually at home, having set up there a laboratory in which friends and relatives acted as his assistants. Plateau himself gave all the instructions to his aids; they reported to him every detail of the results of the experiments and he then dictated the notes covering the work, relying on a remarkable memory. Later the notes would be revised for publication. Plateau supplied the imagination and piercing intelligence; his helpers supplied the eyes and were the reporters. Plateau was the editor. Scientific critics have held that he not only overcame his handicap but actually did better work.

In 1849 Plateau published in the *Bulletin* of the Royal Academy of Belgium further studies on revolving disks and the use of a shutter. This time he also treated the effects when colored, and vari-colored disks are used. The system was similar to the Anorthoscope. Sixteen images were mounted on the margin of a glass disk. Another disk with four slots was revolved four times as swiftly. A number of spectators could see the effect at the same time. The chief illusion was a devil blowing up a fire. Edison's peep-show film machine of 1891 also had a revolving disk with four slots.

The last time Plateau wrote for publication directly on the motion picture machine was in 1852, 20 years after his invention. Once more he had to lash back at critics, this time at those who said he stole not from another of his own time but from the ancient Romans.

In the May 30, 1852 issue of *Cosmos,* a French weekly review of science, edited by Abbé Moigno, comments were made about an article written by one Dr. Sinsteden in the German science review, *Annalen der Physik und Chemie,* which asserted that Lucretius in the fourth book of *De Rerum Natura* described the Fantascope or Phénakisticope invented by Plateau "with such exactitude that, if it were not for the long series of theoretical considerations and practical experiments that led the Belgian scientist to arrive at the construction of the apparatus one would suppose that he took the idea from the Roman philosopher."

To back up the position, the text from Lucretius was quoted in Latin and French and Abbé Moigno made another comment, "What is the effect of that but the Phénakisticope—could Lucretius have described it in terms more precise or more clear?"

Plateau replied in the issue of July 25 of the same year and answered for all time the assertion that Lucretius had invented the first motion picture machine many hundreds of years before.

Moigno realized his mistake and prefaced Plateau's words with an apology, "We are always ready to retract the errors which we print. Our learned friend, Plateau, has written us today about a translation written from a preconceived idea. He has a hundred reasons for complaint."

Plateau's few lines were devastating. He pointed out that the passage of Lucretius used by Dr. Sinsteden and picked up by Abbé Moigno had suppressed one line of the text and had mistranslated others. It was proved that Lucretius was describing not an optical instrument but dreams.

Plateau concluded, "These few words suffice, I hope, to show the true relationship which exists between the passage of Lucretius and the Phénakisticope, and to remove from me all suspicion of having stolen the idea of my instrument from antiquity."

A re-examination of the Latin text of Lucretius leaves no doubt whatsoever that Plateau was correct and Lucretius was writing about dreams and not the first movie device. The lines of Lucretius talk about images, the imagination and dreams. Dr. Sinsteden and others in the 19th century who believed that Lucretius was describing an instrument were confused by failing to understand his words and confusing his theory of vision with an actual piece of apparatus and its effects. It was a simple mistake and accounts for Lucretius' recorded connection with the origin of the motion picture which has been repeated in many books.

A few years before his death Plateau published a complete, annotated bibliography of works on vision from the earliest time to his own day. He started with Aristotle and followed the entire historical trail. About 100 years before his own experiments, the first efforts to measure the persistence of vision were made. All the many years he was blind he was most interested in light, color, vision, the illusion of motion and related phenomena. Plateau regularly attended scientific meetings and his fame was well known throughout the scientific world. He was well known for his religious devotion and piety.

Plateau, honored by his scientific colleagues and the Belgian Government, died at Ghent on September 15, 1883, a few years before the motion picture was presented to the public and acclaimed throughout the world. The art science of magic shadows had made great progress under this Belgian who was endowed with rare talent and an indomitable spirit.

XII

THE BARON'S PROJECTOR

First impact of war on magic shadows—General Uchatius invents a projector combining Kircher's magic lantern and the Plateau-Stampfer picture disks—Motion pictures reach the screen.

THE FIRST MAN to combine Kircher's magic lantern and the Plateau-Stampfer disk and thereby achieve moving images on a screen visible to an audience was Baron General Franz von Uchatius. A type of bronze was named for this Austrian ballistic expert but, though his machine was the pattern for motion picture projectors until the advent of film at the end of the century, his name was not linked with the device. With Uchatius also came the first impact of projected pictures on the science of war. From these small beginnings, in less than a century, the motion picture —in our day—became a great weapon of psychological warfare.

Franz Uchatius, the second son of a former artillery officer and instructor in the cadet school who resigned after 19 years' service to become street commissioner in a small Austrian town, was born on October 20, 1811, at Theresienfeld, Wiener Neustadt, Austria. The father had married a woman from Bavaria and lived comfortably, for in addition to his town job he managed an estate and derived income from an agricultural sowing machine which he had invented.

After elementary and high school education near his home, Franz was apprenticed to a Viennese merchant. His father had to pay an annual fee of some 300 gulden (about $120) for the privilege. Franz, a small, sensitive boy, was very unhappy as an apprentice, having no interest in merchandising. After much persuasion, for his father evidently had found life happier outside the army, Franz received permission to join his eldest brother, Joseph, in the artillery. There was another difficulty. Franz was under the minimum height established for that branch of the army. Special permission had to be received from Archduke Ludwig, the youngest son of Emperor Francis and the general inspector of artillery, before he could enter the artillery school.

But everything was arranged and on August 5, 1829, when Uchatius was 17, he was taken to the Rennweger armory in Vienna to start training as an artillery sub-cadet. Uchatius was especially interested in physics, mathematics and chemistry. Chemistry was not highly regarded then and was usually reserved for non-commissioned officers. Uchatius overcame this prejudice by becoming the laboratory assistant to the professor.

Military advancement came slowly to Uchatius. At 25 he was a gunner but also was able to attend lectures at the Polytechnical School. The next year, 1837, he again became assistant to the chemistry professor at the artillery school, keeping this position until 1841. During that period he served as special tutor to Turkish officers, then studying in Vienna, and also worked in the gun foundry.

Finally in 1843, at the age of 32, he was commissioned a lieutenant. It was at this period that he did his first inventing. A special fuse for guns was his initial achievement. Somewhat later he invented the first European hydrocarbon lamp. This was a special lantern designed for use aboard ship. It was so constructed that it would not go out even when completely overturned. A modification of this lamp was used by Uchatius in one model of his pre-film motion picture projector.

The description of Uchatius' "Apparatus for the presentation of motion pictures upon a wall" was not published until 1853. The account appeared in the *Sitzungsberichte* of the Kaiserliche Akademie der Wissenschaften of Vienna.

But, as Uchatius himself said, he was asked to develop the invention as far back as 1845, at the request of Field Marshal Lieutenant von Hauslab. That general very probably thought that if moving figures of the Plateau-Stampfer magic disks could be projected on the wall there would be available a potent instrument for military instruction. In our own day the motion picture has come to be an important aid in military training all over the world.

Uchatius wrote as follows:

The well known illusion caused by means of the Stampfer disk arises from the fact that the eye receives on the same portion of the retina pictures succeeding one another at short intervals, which present some recurring motion in its various phases, and through this arises an effect which equals that of one picture observed in motion.

The method used by Uchatius to throw a connected series of images on a wall "in any desired size" is indicated by the illustrations.

Uchatius noted that the Plateau-Stampfer disk had a certain disadvantage not only because but one person could observe the effects at a time but also because the pictures were not sharp and clear.

The first model developed by Uchatius was described as follows:

The pictures (a), (a) . . . are painted on transparent glass and mounted on a disk, (A), at equal intervals, and the lowest of the pictures was illuminated from behind by the lamp (S) and the illuminating lens (B). A second disk, (C), contained the slits (b), (b) . . . (the modern shutter) to be brought before each picture. The slits correspond to those in the Stampfer disk. Both disks are mounted on the same axis, (D), and are rotated by the crank (E). The slit, (c), corresponds to the pupil opening of the eye and the achromatic lens, (F), to the crystal lens of the eye. The lens is adjustable to allow the picture to be focussed sharply. The surface, (G) (the screen) finally corresponds to the position of the retina of the eye.

When the disks are turned, the successive pictures appear on the wall, (G), just as they are seen in the Stampfer disk, in intervals so short that they are not noticed by the eye.

This machine was satisfactory but limited. Uchatius was a sharp critic of his own work: "The apparatus produced very good motion pictures whose size, however, could be enlarged to a maximum of only six inches in diameter, because should the wall, (G), be moved far from the projector the pictures became too dark on account of the light cut off by the slits. And an enlargement of the slits brought about greater indistinctness. However, a projected motion picture had been attained which could be viewed simultaneously by a considerable number of people. But it still remained desirable to project this picture in a suitable size on a wall and thus show it in an auditorium or theatre."

The first model had shown that the use of slits, even with the brightest light, could not result in a successful picture, according to Uchatius. (Illustration facing page 105.)

He then constructed the improved model.

The pictures (a), (a) . . . are painted transparently and set upright in a circle as close together as possible on the wooden slide (A). In front of each picture is a projection lens (b), (b) . . . which can be inclined towards the center of the apparatus by means of a hinge and set screw. The inclination of all the projection lenses is so adjusted that their optical axes intersect at the distance at which the picture appears (in other words on the screen). It follows there that all the pictures must appear at one and the same point on the wall, (W).

The light source consists of a lime cylinder, (B) glowing in a stream of oxyhydrogen gas and the condensing lens, (C), which gives somewhat converging rays and illuminates only one picture at a time. The light is turned in a circle by a simple mechanism by means of a crank, (D), either rapidly or slowly as desired, (the first slow motion projector as well). During the movement the light source retains its upright position because of its own weight, since it is suspended from its support, (c), so as to be easily movable. The two rubber gas tubes rise and fall through the opened bottom of the cabinet. The lead weight, (E), serves as a counterweight to the light source.

Uchatius was pleased with this machine. "The result is now evident. The successively illuminated pictures appear on the wall in the same way as the so-called dissolving views but much more rapidly, thereby causing the effect of a moving picture. The size of the picture is not limited by the slits and the sharpness is not affected since no motion of the object picture occurs."

In this manner Uchatius solved the problem of projecting these pre-film hand-painted motion pictures. In the very beginning of magic shadow projection Athanasius Kircher had sought the same results but did not have the apparatus or the knowledge of vision and movement necessary to carry out his wish. The lantern model of Zahn equipped with a revolving disk approximates the plan of Uchatius but failed, as did Kircher's, and for the same reason. So far as Plateau was concerned, the illusion of moving images visible to one person at a time was sufficient. Anyway, the blind man—missing his own sight—probably did not feel impelled toward arranging simultaneous viewing for others. Doubtlessly he thought that to see motion pictures—one person at a time—was a sufficient marvel. Edison, more than half a century later, tended to the same opinion.

Uchatius said that his model projector was equipped with space for twelve pictures painted on glass slides, but he added: "There are no insuperable obstacles in the way of constructing a similar apparatus with 100 pictures, thereby a moving tableau with an action lasting one-half minute could be presented. The apparatus would not need to be more than six feet high."

This shows that Uchatius also was looking ahead to the story motion picture. Until the middle 1890s there were no real motion picture scenes on any screen for more than the one-half minute indicated by Uchatius. His machine was the basic model for four decades and had an influence on the design of many early motion picture projectors and cameras.

Uchatius pointed out that the projector would be useful in demonstrating its own principle in physics and vision classes and could show in a vivid way action of sound waves and "indeed all motions which cannot be demonstrated by mechanism."

The first motion picture projector dealer was W. Prokesch, an optician and lens maker of 46 Lainbruge Street, Vienna, who, Uchatius said, "prepares apparatuses of this sort with greatest precision and upon request also furnishes pictures therefor." Prokesch wrote many years later that the records show that Uchatius began his correspondence with the optical firm about the motion picture projector on February 16, 1851.

It is possible that Uchatius solved the problem of the projector soon after the assignment was given to him by General von Hauslab in 1845. But he was a very busy man from that year, when he became a member of the Academy of Science, until the 1851-53 period when he had time to complete the work, arrange for commercial construction of projectors and write the report for the journal of the Polytechnical School, Akademie der Wissenschaften, *Sitzungsberichte*.

In 1846 Uchatius was given orders to open up a section of the gun foundry and astounded military circles by producing the then great quantity of 10,000 six-pound cannon balls in three months. He taught the Emperor's brothers at the Polytechnical School in 1847. At the age of 37, in 1848, when he had a family of three children and had been in the artillery service for 19 years, he received a promotion to first lieutenant. Advancement was slow because this extremely talented man had no influence in political circles.

In 1848 Uchatius was assigned to Italy and assisted at the siege of Venice. There he started the unenviable precedent of the aerial bombardment of cities. In three weeks he had constructed more than 100 balloons fitted to carry explosive charges to be dropped on the heads of the "besieged, rebellious Venetians." Uchatius and his brother, Joseph, studied the problem on the spot. The experiment was only partially successful. The Venetians were probably as terrified by rumor of bombs falling from the heavens as were the invaders under Marcellus before Syracuse when Archimedes developed his Burning Glasses.

Uchatius' relations with the Navy which was directing the siege were not the best and he was glad to be able to return to Vienna. During the next few years he continued to make little progress in the military world but was doing excellent scientific work. He began to test guns and had an opportunity to travel and inspect foreign ordnance and manufacturing methods. In 1867, at the age of 56, he received his first important recognition. He was decorated for his work and made colonel commander of the artillery ordnance factory in 1871. Previously he had helped to direct the construction of the arsenal at Vienna.

In 1874 he developed the first steel-bronze cannon out of "Uchatius" bronze. Through the next few years he carried on a struggle for the establishment of a native ordnance industry so that Austria would not depend upon a foreign munitions supplier. Some in authority wanted the heavy guns made at Krupp, in Prussia, but Uchatius finally won and was promoted to the rank of major-general by the Emperor, given the Commander's Cross of the Order of St. Stephen, a lifetime personal annual bonus of 2,000 gulden, together with baronship.

Uchatius' weapons were used by Austria in the occupation at Bosnia and Herzegovnia in 1878-79, when the Turks withdrew, in accordance with the Treaty of Berlin.

It is easy to see that a man of such activity had no time to further work on the motion picture projector which he had invented as a young man, passing away tedious years while awaiting promotion and responsibility.

Eventually Uchatius became a Field Marshal, but he died unhappy. He wrote a farewell note, "Forgive me, my dear ones, because I am unable to endure life any longer," and killed himself on June 4, 1881, at the age of 69. He was broken-hearted. Though his artillery weapons had been a great success, he had yet to perfect coast defense guns. The final blow was a remark passed on from the Austrian War Department, that the officials doubted they would live to see successful completion of Uchatius' coastal guns. Also, an order was sent to Krupp for four such guns for the harbor of Pola, then an Austro-Hungarian seaport, and after World War II, a port in the area disputed by Italy and Yugoslavia. It was said that the general was ill, suffering from an incurable cancer of the stomach.

Uchatius was naturally a hero of the Austrian artillery. A monumental obelisk was raised to his memory by subscriptions from the men who were using his weapons. His biographer, Karl Spacîl, wrote: "As often as this country (Austria) begins to re-arm, it is no wonder that the name of Uchatius is mentioned and praised anew."

But Uchatius then and now should have been praised not for his engines of war but for his important contribution to the magic shadow art-science. For by perfecting a motion picture machine which would bring living pictures before audiences, Uchatius, together with Kircher and Plateau, the other great magic shadow pioneers, deserves credit and the gratitude of untold millions who down through the years have had their lives enriched through this great new medium of expression.

The use of Uchatius' projector spread rapidly. It satisfied a natural urge. Man from the beginning sought to recreate life naturally and realistically. Large screen motion pictures, even of but one scene, repeated over and over, represented a definite step on that road.

Within a few years after the publication of accounts of the Uchatius motion picture projector, models were brought out by English and French inventors. Projectors, including one which threw onto a screen by means of a mirror system images of living

Abb. 1. Franz Freiherr von Uchatius.

Ölbildnis von Sigmund l'Allemand im Besitz des Wiener Heeresmuseums.

Schweizerische Zeitschrift, 1905

FRANZ VON UCHATIUS in 1853 combined Kircher's projector of 1645 and Plateau's revolving disk of 1832 to achieve the first projection of animated designs.

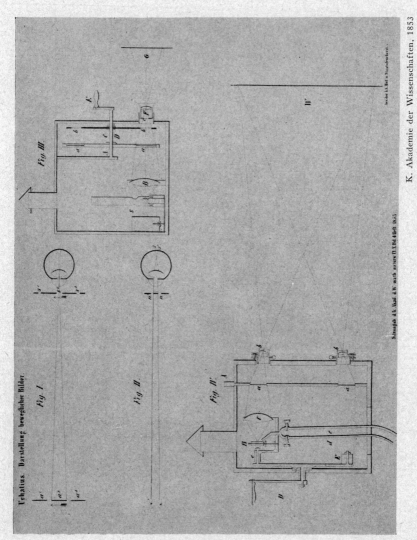

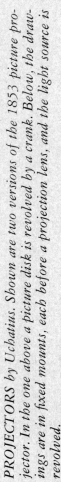

PROJECTORS by Uchatius. Shown are two versions of the 1853 picture projector. In the one above a picture disk is revolved by a crank. Below, the drawings are in fixed mounts, each before a projection lens, and the light source is
revolved.

persons, were used at the London Polytechnic Institute.

For many years after the announcement of the Uchatius picture projector, only hand-drawn designs were used. The new photographs were available only in single stills. But now the modern motion picture was just around a not too distant corner.

XIII

THE LANGENHEIMS OF PHILADELPHIA

*⤳Brothers Langenheim perfect a sys-
tem of printing photographs on glass
slides permitting projection on the
screen—Projectors are made by Duboscq in France; Wheatstone and
Claudet in England; Brown and Heyl in
the United States.*

WILLIAM PENN'S "City of Brotherly Love", Philadelphia,
was the home of several important American contributors
to the magic shadow art-science. The first of these were two brothers, Frederic and William Langenheim.

William Langenheim came to the United States from Germany
in 1834, the year Ebenezer Strong Snell, a professor at Amherst
College, introduced in America the Plateau-Stampfer magic disks.
Successively, he served in Texas during its war for independence
from Mexico; was present at the recapture of the Alamo by
American forces; was captured himself and sentenced to be shot;
escaped, and served in the United States Army in the Second
Florida Seminole War.

After three years of adventure, William decided in 1840 to
settle in Philadelphia and enter business. He had his brother,
Frederic, come to America to be his partner. Frederic Langenheim
brought to his brother news of the latest developments in photography and they decided to embark upon that pursuit. The year
before, 1839, Louis Jacques Mande Daguerre (1789-1851), in
France, and William Henry Fox Talbot (1800-1877), in England, had announced successful still pictures made with a modified

portable form of our old friend, the *camera obscura,* fitted with a chemically coated plate which after development made the picture permanent.

Frederic Langenheim was familiar with all these advances when he came to Philadelphia in 1840 and he either brought with him a good camera or one was ordered from Vienna shortly afterwards. In the winter of 1840-41 the Langenheim brothers opened a studio at the Merchant's Exchange, 3rd and Walnut Streets, Philadelphia. They were not the first photographers in the United States but were among the pioneers.

Pictures from the size of a pea to very large ones were advertised. President Tyler and Henry Clay were among those who sat for Langenheim. In an early adventure in the use of photography for advertising, the Langenheims had something less than a complete success, from the client's point of view. A picture was made showing a number of prominent persons drinking at a local establishment. It was not good for business—a rigorous public objected to the "drinking scene."

Frederic, who was the "outside man" of the business and the principal photographer of natural subjects—William handled the business end and the portraits—went to Niagara Falls in 1845 and made scene pictures that brought fame and renown to the firm of Langenheim Bros. Copies were sent to Queen Victoria, the Kings of Prussia, Saxony and Wurtenberg and the Duke of Brunswick, the province in Germany whence the brothers originally came; and to Daguerre himself. The latter praised the successful photography in a letter transmitted to the Langenheims.

In 1848 William went abroad and in England concluded a deal with William Henry Fox Talbot, British pioneer in photography, giving the Langenheims exclusive contract rights to the Talbot calotype process which used a negative from which any number of paper prints could be made. It was a vast improvement over the Daguerreotype negative-positive system which did not make possible printing of copies but the Langenheims were not successful in sub-licensing the Talbot process in America.

Shortly after this the Langenheims made an important contribution to the art-science of light and shadow pictures by developing a system which made it possible to project the photographs in the old Kircher magic lantern. This prepared the way for the projection of a series of photographs showing a single movement.

Kircher and the others who used his magic lantern, including the projection model of Uchatius, painted or drew their various scenes on glass slides. Until about 1850 when the Langenheim development was announced, there was no satisfactory method of making glass plates of positive photographs. Of course, the heat of the projecting lamp made it impossible to use pictures printed on paper.

Frederic Langenheim, with U. S. patent No. 7,784, dated November 19, 1850, solved the problem. The Langenheim system was called "Hyalotype," from the Greek, meaning "glass" and "to print" or to print on glass. Prior to the invention, some time in the winter of 1847-48, the period of the California Gold Rush, it was said the Langenheims, by means of a Viennese camera converted into a magic lantern equipped with a gas lamp, projected Daguerreotype pictures. This probably was achieved with the aid of a mirror system.

The early Langenheim glass projector slides were circular and of a deep sepia tint; later excellent black-and-white plates were made. The Langenheim glass photo slides reproduced nature on the screen "with fidelity truly astonishing." The two plates of the slide were made adherent with Canada Balsam, which is still used in this way as well as to attach parts of projection lens systems. Only very recently have new synthetic resins begun to displace Canada Balsam for these purposes.

In 1851 the Langenheim Hyalotypes made their debut in Europe under great auspices, at the famous Exposition of the Works of All Nations at London. The glass projection photos were "very remarkable and well appreciated by competent visitors," according to Robert Hunt, a pioneer British photographic authority, who inspected the exhibit and wrote about it.

There is no evidence that the Langenheims combined their glass projection slides with the magic disk of Plateau to achieve motion pictures. They made one contribution and seemed to be satisfied with that. And it was successful for them, for in the next twenty-five years many thousands of these slides were sold in the United States.

Others who perhaps were much more familiar with the Plateau-Stampfer magic disks than the Langenheims combined their process with the Wheel of Life. The link nevertheless with the Langenheims is direct and immediate. All the followers used the photos on glass slides and the method was popularized by the Langenheim exhibition at the Exposition. Relatively little was done, however, in combining the glass photo slides in motion picture sequence with the magic lantern, because at the time there was no method of obtaining a number of successive photos of the same action.

Jules Duboscq (1817-1886) in Paris copied the Langenheim process of glass plates with great success. Duboscq was an exhibitor of optical instruments at the Exposition of 1851. He had been the licensee of Daguerre for England, but the method was never popular there as it was in the United States. On February 16, 1852, Duboscq received a French patent on an apparatus which combined photos and the Plateau Phénakisticope or Fantascope. His device was called the Stereofantascope or Bioscope.

One Duboscq model had two strips of pictures made with a binocular camera running next to each other on a vertical disk, as the original Plateau model, and the whole was rapidly revolved before a mirror by a spectator who wore specially-made glasses. The second and better system had the pictures mounted on the horizontal Fantascope or Wheel of Life, as developed by Horner in 1834, with one picture mounted above the other. There was, however, slight distortion because the pictures were bent to fit around the inside of the cylinder.

Sir Charles Wheatstone (1802-1875), who also combined photos and the magic disk, in 1852, had a marked influence on magic picture development during the middle part of the 19th century. In fact, it may well be that the efforts expended in trying to combine the third dimensional effect of his stereoscope with the magic disk retarded development of screen projection of motion pictures.

Wheatstone was a timid man, though a great scientist, and frequently had the great Michael Faraday announce his inventions at the Royal Society meetings. The Stereoscope was invented in 1838. (The reader may recall that centuries before d'Aguilon had coined the name "Stereo" for "seeing solid" effects). The Stereoscope achieves its effect by blending into one image pictures or drawings of an object taken from slightly different points of view so that the impression of relief is obtained in our sense of vision. Without our two eyes the stereoscopic effect would not be possible.

It had been known for a very long time that the two eyes did not see the identical picture. Wheatstone made an instrument which took advantage of this fact. He said he conceived the idea in 1835 and made the first presentation of the Stereoscope in August of 1838 at a meeting of the British Association held at Newcastle.

In 1850 Wheatstone was in Paris and showed his improved Stereoscope to Abbé Moigno, to Soleil and his son-in-law, Duboscq, who were commercial instrument makers, and to members of the French Institute. Its value was immediately recognized not only for amusement but for the arts and sciences, especially portraiture and sculpture, Moigno reported in *La Presse* of December 28, 1850. Duboscq immediately started to make one and used Daguerreotypes in it. Moigno praised Duboscq's "intelligence, activity, affability, indefatigable ardour." In 1851 Moigno brought Duboscq to the attention of the Queen by presenting her with a Wheatstone-type Stereoscope which he had made. That was the year Louis Napoleon seized power and was named president for a ten year term. In November, 1852 he proclaimed himself Emperor.

Wheatstone also developed a combination of photos and the Plateau disk which was fitted with a cog which made each photo rest momentarily as it was held before the mirror. The same instrument was made in France under the name of Heliocine-graphe.

Antoine François Jean Claudet (1797-1867), was a Frenchman who married an English girl and moved to London in 1827. In 1852 he combined the Plateau-Stampfer disk with the Langenheim method of photographs on glass plates. It is claimed that, while Claudet started work ahead of him, Duboscq had satisfactory results first. Claudet's experiments were successful in May of 1852, about one year after the Langenheim exhibit at the Exposition. In 1853 Claudet became a member of the Royal Society.

Claudet, at a meeting of the British Association for the Advancement of Science held at Birmingham in September, 1865, spoke "On Moving Photographic figures, illustrating some phenomena of vision connected with the combination of the stereoscope and the phenakisticope by means of photography." Claudet noted that from the beginning of photography those acquainted with Plateau's disk thought that pictures would be more suitable than hand drawings to show the illusions of motion. But they also sought the third dimensional effect. Duboscq's efforts were not completely successful, according to Claudet who described a machine he had worked out. The illusion of motion was effected by having one eye see one picture and the other eye the next picture. This resulted in a simultaneous motion and solid effect. The spectator was not conscious of the vision being transferred from one eye to another. Claudet's example was a boxer about to strike and then delivering the blow.

The pictures in Claudet's machine must have left much to the imagination but an interesting perfection of this device was shown in New York in late 1922 and early 1923, under the name of Hammond's Teleview. An entire theatre was equipped with a special shutter device for each spectator. The shutters were synchronized with the shutter of the motion picture projector and the spectator, looking through the device, saw motion in three dimensions. The development was not commercially practicable because the apparatus was expensive, a nuisance to the spectators and the many little motors operating the shutters created an annoying hum in the auditorium.

In the United States the Langenheim brothers did much to popularize the Stereoscope and its various modifications. About 1850 they started to make and sell stereoscopic views in Philadelphia, by mail and through agents throughout the country. In those days, with the Gold Rush in California just subsiding, there was great interest in scenic wonders and views of remote places. Stereoscopic photos had a great sale and were eventually found in almost every parlor of the day.

Before the Civil War the Langenheims opened at 188 Chestnut Street the "Stereoscope Cosmorama Exhibit." There each spectator sat and could see one stereoscopic view after another by turning a crank. It may very well have been this turning crank system which suggested an interesting motion picture device to the fellow citizen of Langenheims, Coleman Sellers.

Coleman Sellers (1827-1907) was a skilled engineer. He reproduced Faraday's electric experiments in this country; constructed locomotives in Cincinnati chiefly for the Panama Railroad; he also worked on the Niagara Falls power development. Even for hobbies he turned to scientific toys and gadgets. In 1856 he was called to Philadelphia again to take his place in the family engineering company. Sellers' family dated from one Samuel Sellers who received a royal grant of land in Pennsylvania in 1682.

Sellers patented on February 5, 1861 a device which he called the Kinematoscope, evidently the first use of the word "cinema" if we exclude the Frenchman who copied Wheatstone's device under the name of Quinetoscope.

The Sellers device revolved a series of posed still pictures, paddle-wheel fashion, before the eye of the observer. A period of relative rest was achieved through this motion as each picture was coming towards the observer for a specific time and then out of view as the next photo came into position. Sellers' motion photos include his wife sewing, his two sons, Coleman, Jr. and Horace, playing and rocking a chair. Sellers tried to combine motion and solid effects. He found the wet plate photographic process invented by Frederick Scott Archer (1813-1857) in 1850 quite unsatisfactory for "posed" motion work. Archer did not trouble to patent the process.

During the Civil War the Langenheims took nearly 1,000 pictures which were mounted for showing in the projection magic lanterns, and during the Franco-Prussian War in 1870-71 several hundred photographs and drawings were released by the Langenheim brothers for lantern use. The last catalogue of the firm was published in 1874 and included some 6,000 colored slides priced at $33 a dozen, and those specially photographed and made at $4 each. William Langenheim died on May 4, 1874. Frederic tried to continue the business for a time but he, too, was getting old and eventually sold out in the Autumn to Caspar W. Briggs, another early Philadelphia photographer. At the Philadelphia exhibit Frederic had a showing of the Voigtlander lenses made in Vienna which were the best then available for certain types of photographic work.

Another Philadelphian, Henry Renno Heyl (1842-1919), a friend and associate of Sellers on the Board of Trustees of the Franklin Institute, was the first person in America to develop a projector which used "posed" motion photographs. The individual pictures were taken by the same method used by Sellers for his Kinematoscope.

Somewhat earlier, O. B. Brown, of Malden, Mass. obtained U. S. patent No. 93,594, dated August 10, 1869, on what is the first American "motion picture" projector. It, however, used only drawn designs and not photographs. In principle it was based, as other projectors of the time, on the system developed by Uchatius. In

LANGENHEIM BROTHERS, William (seated) and Frederic, pioneer Philadelphia photographers, who developed, in 1850, picture projection using glass slides.

ETIENNE JULES MAREY, *French physiologist, whose research on the movement of men and animals contributed to progress in photography of motion, 1870 to 1890.*

Brown's projector the Plateau magic disk with the figures was mounted between the light source and the projection lens and was rotated by a gear arrangement. In front of the lens there was a rotating shutter with two holes which interrupted the light when the pictures were in intermittent motion.

Heyl perhaps may have obtained his basic idea from Brown or it may have come to him independently because the urge to combine the new photos and the older magic lantern was felt by many persons. At any rate, the Heyl apparatus bears very little relation to Brown's. There is no evidence that Heyl attempted to patent his device, so the Patent Office never was called upon to decide the point.

Heyl, a native of Columbus, Ohio, who designed many types of machinery, including boxes and paper and book stitching devices, has been hailed by some as the first to use photos in a projection device. He himself, however, never claimed that honor. He published a letter dated Philadelphia, February 1, 1898, in the *Journal* of the Franklin Institute, "A contribution to the history of the art of photographing living subjects in motion and reproducing the natural movements by the lantern."

"Among the earliest public exhibitions" of such a combination was one given by him at an entertainment held in the Academy of Music, in Philadelphia on February 5, 1870. A catalogue note announced as a feature of the varied entertainment the showing of "The Phasmatrope, a most recent scientific invention," whose effects are similar "to the familiar toy called the Zoetrope." The management expressed pleasure at having "the first opportunity of presenting its merits to our audience."

Heyl and a dancing partner posed for six pictures in the various phases of the waltz at O. H. Willard's photographic studio at 1206 Chestnut Street. Other photo slides were made of a then popular Japanese acrobatic performer—"Little All Right." The time exposures were taken on wet plates, then prints were transferred to thin glass plates with the images only about three quarters of an inch high.

The six stills were duplicated three times to fill the eighteen spaces in the wheel of the projector.

The Heyl projector had an intermittent movement controlled by a ratchet and pawl mechanism operated by a reciprocating bar moved up and down by the hand. The fast movement was used

for the acrobats with a complete stop at the end of each somer-
sault, and a slow tempo for the waltz which was accompanied
by an orchestra.

The problem of a shutter to interrupt the light while the pictures were moving was solved in the following way, according to
Heyl: "This was accomplished by a vibrating shutter placed back
of the picture wheel that was operated on the same drawbar that
moved the wheel, only the shutter movement was so timed that it
moved first and covered the picture before the latter moved and
completed the movement after the next picture was in place. This
movement reduced to a great extent the flickering and gave very
natural and life-like representations of the moving figures."

Heyl's Phasmatrope was an ingenious apparatus but the imagination had to compensate for its many imperfections. When it
was demonstrated on March 16, 1870, at a meeting of the Franklin
Institute, it created so little notice that mention of the showing was
not included in the minutes. It is interesting to note it was at
this meeting that Sellers was elected head of the Franklin Insitute.
We can wonder what his reaction was to the fact that Heyl, a man
fifteen years his junior, had added projection to the principle of his
Kinematoscope which had also used "posed pictures" in a peep-
show apparatus.

In 1875, in Philadelphia, Caspar Briggs, who had bought out
the Langenheim interest the year before, introduced a device similar to the Heyl projector which also used still photographs made
of drawings to simulate motion. His most popular subject was
"The Dancing Skeleton," a selection reminiscent of Phantasmagoria and the "black arts" or necromancy. The little pictures were
mounted on the edge of a mica disk which revolved before the
projection lens. Briggs also improved the Langenheim magic lantern slide process and gave a further impetus to photographic
activity in Philadelphia.

From the Langenheims and their contemporaries in America
the spotlight of magic shadow development shifts back to the Old
World, to France, and to a scientist of distinction.

XIV

MAREY AND MOVEMENT

⌐Marey in Paris, and Muybridge and Isaacs in San Francisco, record motion by photographs—Ducos du Hauron has an idea for a complete system—Janssen makes a "movie" camera—Reynauld keeps magic shadow showmanship alive —Anschütz uses electricity.

THE DEVELOPMENT capital in the story of the magic shadow art-science shifted many times. Seas, mountains, oceans and time itself were no barriers. Successively, Greece, Arabia, Persia, England, Italy, Holland, Belgium, Austria and the United States took the lead in showing the way toward the goal of genuinely life-like pictures. After the great spurt of activity in Philadelphia, during the working life of the Langenheims, the chief center of activity was Paris and the leader was Etienne Jules Marey.

Plateau in Belgium came to the invention of the magic disk, which was the first "motion picture" device, through his study of vision and the desire to understand more about it. Marey, by his own action and the work of others influenced by him, gave great impetus to the photographing and projection of motion pictures, through his wish to learn more about movement, the movement of life—animals, birds, and men.

Marey was one of the first great physiologists and conducted for years what was then the only private, scientific laboratory in France. He was born in Beaume, France, in 1830, and when nineteen went to Paris to study medicine. Six years later he became an interne and, in 1859, received his doctor's degree, doing at this time his first important work on animal locomotion. In 1869 he became a professor at the College of France and three years later he was admitted to the Academy of Medicine, and, in 1878, to the Academy of Science.

About 1867 Marey started to study the attitudes of animals in movement through the aid of a Plateau magic disk and drawings made with the aid of Mathias Duval, professor of anatomy at the School of Beaux Arts. Some of the designs used by Marey in the Wheel of Life and a magic lantern projector were drawn by Col. Duhousset, a great horseman and artist, from very early and imperfect instantaneous photographs.

Prior to Marey there had been a number of attempts to record motion by photography. The most successful was by the French astronomer, Pierre Jules César Janssen (1824-1907) who used a photogun, *Revolver Photographique,* to record the transit of Venus in Japan in 1874. Janssen may have been influenced by Marey's earliest work. Dr. R. L. Maddox in 1871 had developed in England dry plate photography, based on Scott Archer's wet plate process. This helped to make instantaneous photography, or Chronophotography, as it was called, possible.

Janssen perfected the first workable motion picture camera. But it was a large, stationary piece of apparatus, limited in scope and sensitiveness. The device was described by a French astronomer, C. Flammarion, in the magazine *La Nature* of May 8, 1875, and by Janssen himself in the *Bulletin of the French Photographic Societies* of April 7, 1876. Janssen's device took forty-eight pictures on a simple revolving plate but he said the number could easily be doubled or tripled. A time clock mechanism controlled the revolutions of the photographic plate but it was so arranged that it could also be rotated by hand. An electrical hook-up also was possible.

The influence of Plateau's magic disk is clear and so acknowledged by Janssen. The device simply reversed the old Plateau disk which showed motion pictures through two revolving disks, one with the pictures and the other with the shutter slits. In the Janssen astronomical gun the one disk was coated with photographic chemicals and the other had the usual slits; the necessary intermittent movement was provided by the gear driven mechanism which rotated the disks.

Janssen pointed out that the apparatus could be used for physiological purposes—to study walking, running, flight and the movement of animals; but he never had time to develop the device for physiological uses, which was not in his immediate field. He was, however, interested in Marey's later refinements and applications.

The most important "precursor" of motion picture photography and projection, so far as the basic idea was concerned, was Louis Ducos du Hauron (1837-1920), a Frenchman who developed the first successful method of printing color pictures. Louis liked science, painting and music but was held back in school on account of poor health. At the age of 15, he was a good pianist. He began his experiments in natural color printing around 1859 and by the Fall of 1868 had achieved success. The public reaction was not enthusiastic and Louis became discouraged. Many persons were hostile to his method which he hoped would bring books, illustrated with many color plates, within reach of everyone (as others following his system eventually achieved). It was for this reason that he failed to exploit his camera and picture projector idea.

In March and December of 1864 Louis Ducos du Hauron took out the first patents on a complete motion picture system, including an apparatus to register and reproduce motion by photography. The French patent was described in these words, "Apparatus for the photographic reproduction of any view together with all changes the subject undergoes during a certain time." A mechanic of Agen where Louis lived for many years with his older brother, Alcide, constructed a model of the device. It was not successful because the available photographic materials were not sufficiently sensitive. Ducos' patent even provided for the use of "bands" of paper; bands or reels of film finally solved the motion picture problem but not until near the end of the 19th century. As in one of Uchatius' projectors, the camera and projector of Louis Ducos du Hauron used a number of small lenses.

Other patents taken out by this small, slender, timid Frenchman who only became truly animated when talking about one of his inventions, included color photography in 1868, a horizontal windmill in 1869, a combined natural and photographic camera in 1874, photographic devices in 1888 and 1892. In 1896 he again turned to motion pictures, after others had perfected them, proposing an optical system intended to do away with all interruption of light in motion picture projection and photography.

Honors came very late in life to Ducos du Hauron and to his dying day he reproached himself for not exploiting sufficiently his ideas. But when he had tried to do this he encountered only indifference because the scientists were not interested in the work of one who was without academic status. Now Ducos du Hauron is regarded as one of the greatest geniuses of photography. He actually predicted and described a monopack color film. The many good color processes of this type are modern realizations of his extraordinary scientific analyses.

Marey was familiar in a general way with all these developments and ideas, but he was essentially a scientist and not a photographer. Motion picture photography to him was just a good way of learning more about living movement. About 1870 he had made studies of movements in other ways in addition to primitive photographs and drawings made from such photographs. The results of these studies were known all over the world and had a direct influence on the photographers who first successfully took successive pictures of animals in motion. These photographers were Eadweard Muybridge and John D. Isaacs.

Eadweard Muybridge (1830-1904), or Edward James Muggeridge, as he was originally named, was born in England, at Kingston-on-Thames. As a young man he was an adventurer who called photography his profession. He made a number of trips back and forth between the United States and England. He was seriously injured in a run-away stage coach accident in July of 1860, in Arkansas, and later obtained several thousand dollars in damages from the Southern Overland Stage Company. Returning to the United States after a visit in England, following the accident, Muybridge received an assignment to photograph, for the United States Coast and Geodetic Survey, the new territory of Alaska, purchased by the United States in 1867. After this assignment he settled in San Francisco.

In 1872 Governor Leland Stanford of California made a $25,000 bet in connection with a dispute as to whether or not all the legs of a horse running at a full gallop are off the ground simultaneously. The eye was not quick enough to find the answer. Horsemen had never been completely satisfied with the drawings and pictures made by artists of horses in motion. Sanford, as Terry Ramsaye describes in his history of the motion picture, *A Million and One Nights,* in 1872 sent for the photographer Muybridge and had him go to the Sacramento race track to get photographic proof in order to settle the dispute. Over a period of years Stanford

spent considerably more than the $25,000 wager on the photo-
graphic experiments. And out of the experiments grew the legend
that Muybridge had invented "motion pictures."

About 1870 Marey had established the movement of the legs
of a horse in a gallop through his physiological investigations.
But at that time he had no photographic proof of his theory. Years
later Muybridge said that Stanford obtained his basic ideas for
photographs to win the bet from the writings of Marey.

Muybridge might have been successful in his early experiments
if it had not been for an interruption which was of about five years'
duration. He had domestic troubles of a nature that ended in
violence. In October 1874, he shot and killed Major Harry Larkyn
who had eloped with his wife. After a sensational trial in which
the defense was able to succeed in putting the jurors mentally in
Muybridge's place, he was acquitted on February 5, 1875, at the
courthouse in Napa, California.

Stanford maintained a friendly interest in Muybridge because
he had become increasingly interested in the problem of the movements of a horse in fast action and he wished to obtain evidence
to confirm the new theory of animal locomotion which had been
developed chiefly by Marey in France. Stanford was primarily
interested in the running gaits of horses and other movements
secondarily.

The stories of what really happened in 1877 are not identical.
Muybridge said in 1883 at a lecture at the Franklin Institute in
Philadelphia, "Being much interested with the experiments of
Professor Marey . . . I invented a method of employing a number of cameras .. . . I explained my intended experiments to a
wealthy resident of San Francisco, Mr. Stanford, who liberally
agreed to place the resources of his stock breeding farm at my
disposal and to reimburse the expenses of my investigation, upon
the condition of my supplying him, for his private use, with a
few copies of the contemplated results."

On the mere statement, Muybridge's position is subject to serious
question. It certainly is unlikely that Stanford would pay all expenses just to obtain a few copies of the "intended results for private use." The ownership of the results was subject to considerable
dispute. Stanford copyrighted the pictures in 1881 and had them
published in a book edited by Dr. J. D. B. Stillman, entitled *The
Horse in Motion*. In that book the story is that when Muybridge

returned to San Francisco in 1877, he was engaged to continue the experiments by Stanford. According to Stillman, in 1877 pictures were taken of one of Stanford's horses, with a single camera and "one of these, representing him with all his feet clear of the ground, was enlarged, retouched and distributed to the parties interested." This then was just another effort to obtain a good, sharp, fast, single picture of action.

John D. Isaacs, later chief engineer for the Harriman Railroad System, had designed and supervised all the installation of the battery camera apparatus. His name was suggested to Stanford by Arthur Brown, then chief engineer of maintenance of the Central Pacific, one of Stanford's interests. Isaacs was a young man fresh from the University of Virginia, where he had graduated in 1875. He was an amateur photographer and very familiar with Marey's work and that of the photographers in France and England and in the eastern part of the United States.

In 1878 further efforts were made at Stanford's private track at Palo Alto, where the battery system of cameras was introduced and good results obtained. Each camera in the battery was equipped with a fast-acting shutter and was set off successively by a mechanical-electrical device. (Illustration on opposite page.)

The most successful results, which were little better than silhouettes, were obtained when twenty-four cameras, set about one foot apart, were used. The photographs actually were not made at equal intervals of time but of space. The cameras and background were lined up for a measurement of distance and not of time.

Although Isaacs contributed engineering skill to the development of the apparatus, because he was chiefly interested in railroad engineering and this assignment in his photographic hobby was a favor for the "big boss," Muybridge alone obtained the patents on the method. On June 27 and July 11, 1878 he applied for a patent on, "A method and apparatus for photographing objects in motion" (the battery system), and for the double action shutter controls. The patents were issued in March, 1879. Wet collodion plates were used in each camera and a speed of up to 1/5000th of a second was claimed by Muybridge in his applications. Isaacs later became chief engineer of the Southern Pacific Railroad System while Muybridge made "scientific" photography a profession.

During later life Muybridge sought to establish himself as a

The Horse in Motion, 1882

CAMERA SYSTEM developed by John D. Isaacs, engineer, and Eadweard Muybridge, photographer, which made pictures at equal intervals of space rather than of time. It settled a wager on the nature of the movements of a horse.

La Nature, 1882

PHYSIOLOGICAL PARK, Paris, above, the first motion picture studio. Marey installed the camera in a box on rails. Below, Marey's photo gun, first portable camera for photographing motion.

scientist and in this effort he drew heavily on physiological data which originated with Marey in France. Muybridge was a photographer who, through the resources of Stanford, a rich and determined backer, came into possession of a method of taking successive pictures of action. Even though the method was cumbersome and inexact, Muybridge never changed it but continued to exploit it for the rest of his life.

Marey, in France, was delighted to hear of the results of Muybridge's work and to inspect them, for here at last was excellent confirmation of his physiological theories. Marey, while praising the work of Muybridge, noted certain errors resulting from the battery camera system—the landscape and not the animal appeared to be moving when the resulting photographs were analyzed in the Plateau magic disk and also the time interval, as noted above, was not exact.

Marey was the first to synthesize motion from the photographs by mounting them so the action could be reconstructed. Muybridge had no interest in this phase of the subject until he met Marey and learned from him. Even afterwards Muybridge continued to be interested chiefly in taking pictures and not in studying and analyzing them. Technically speaking, Marey analyzed and synthesized the results obtained in the Muybridge photographs.

In addition to using the simple Plateau disk which only one person at a time could see, Marey somewhat later had the photographs copied on glass slides, mounted on a revolving disk and projected onto a screen with the Uchatius type projector, equipped with a revolving slit shutter. This scientific demonstration was the first actual motion picture show of real motion and not posed as in the Heyl, Bourbouze and other demonstrations of about 1870.

Gaston Tissandier, editor of *La Nature,* in the December 7, 1878, issue wrote on "The Attitudes of the Horse, represented by instantaneous photography," and discussed the photographs of Eadweard Muybridge of San Francisco which were on display at the firm of Brandon and Morgan Brown, 1, Rue Lafitte, Paris. The early work of Marey was mentioned and the importance of the new pictures was stressed.

On December 28, 1878, a letter of Marey's, published in *La Nature,* expressed the hope that Muybridge would also record and analyze the action of birds in flight as well as animals in motion. Marey mentioned how effective such pictures would be in the

Wheel of Life disks and their value in zoology. There also Marey spoke of a photographic gun which he was to invent later.

A return letter from Muybridge was published on February 17, 1879 in the same magazine: "Please have the goodness to transmit to Professor Marey the assurance of my highest esteem and tell him that the reading of his celebrated book on animal mechanism had inspired Governor Stanford with the first idea of the possibility of solving the problem of locomotion with the aid of photography. Mr. Stanford consulted me in this matter and, on his request, I decided to undertake the task. He asked me to follow a most complete series of experiments." Muybridge said also that he was using as many as thirty cameras, mounted twelve inches apart, and that he planned to study all movements, including flights of birds in which Marey was so interested at the time.

In the March 17 issue of *La Nature*, Marey expressed pleasure that Muybridge was undertaking study of birds in flight. In the same issue there appeared an interesting letter from Eugene Vassel, Captain of Armament at the Suez Canal, dated January 20, 1879, commenting on Marey's idea of a photographic gun and telling of an idea for a similar automatic camera. This illustrates that at the time, even at the ends of the earth, farthest removed from principal educational and scientific centers, the problem of photographing objects in natural movement was under study. It was then a long way, indeed, from Paris to San Francisco to Suez.

By 1880 Plateau magic disks equipped with Muybridge photographs were on sale in England and at about the same time in France. In the December 31, 1881, issue of *La Nature* several of these were illustrated and the possibilities of their use for instruction and entertainment were discussed. It was evident that they were common as toys in Paris. Subjects included the original one of a horse in motion and even a comedy item of a mule kicking a ball.

Muybridge, in the Summer of 1881, went to Paris and there came directly under the influence of Marey who was always most generous in expressing his appreciation of valued work. In this Marey's nature reminds one of Plateau, the Belgian. Evidently Muybridge had not dreamed of the importance of his pictures for physiological study and other such purposes until it was explained to him. It was the pressing quest of Marey for greater perfection in duplicating nature that gave a great stimulus to the development of the motion picture art-science. Perhaps he, too, would have been surprised had he known that the motion picture, while a great instrument of science, would for many years at least find its chief use as an entertainment medium. To the last, Marey always thought of it for science and, while he did not disdain amusement uses, his interest was exclusively in broadening the field of knowledge.

In Paris Muybridge met many notables, including Jean Louis Ernest Meissonier (1815-1891), French painter who specialized in great detail and exact duplication of nature. Meissonier appreciated the value of the Muybridge photos, as he did Marey's work in analyzing motion in animals and men, as an aid to painting. From that time on Meissonier always kept a Plateau disk and projection device in his studio so that photographs of objects which were to be painted could be studied first by himself and his colleagues. Muybridge evidently took a liking to Meissonier and his work because he singled him out in later years as a painter (one of the few) who was exact in his representation of animals in movement even before the evidence of instantaneous photographs was available.

During his visit in Paris Muybridge not only obtained scientific knowledge from Marey and his associates but took up a practical projection device, even to the extent of appropriating the name from Charles Reynaud, a French inventor who was later to be the first great motion picture showman, even though he preferred using hand-drawn films to photographs.

Charles Emile Reynaud (1844-1918) in 1877 developed the Praxinoscope which was an ingenious arrangement of the Plateau magic disk device. The several pictures were mounted on the inside of a horizontal wheel and were viewed on a polygonal-mirror in the center. In this device a number of spectators could watch the moving figures. Light was reflected from a lamp mounted above. Photographs were also used in various of the Praxinoscope models. It was useful for color research. In an article in *La Nature* of February 1, 1879, it was stated that Mr. Reynaud had already planned a projection model which would throw life-size figures from the Praxinoscope onto a screen before a large audience. In 1880 the French Society of Photographers was asked to interest itself in this problem.

In 1881, or in the following year, Reynaud achieved success

with the Projection Praxinoscope or Lamposcope described by Gaston Tissandier, in the November 4, 1882, issue of *La Nature*. One lantern threw the background and the moving device projected the motion pictures. The designs were colored on glass slides which were joined in a band. A special advantage of the Reynaud Projection Praxinoscope or Lamposcope was that no special light source was required. A common table lamp was suitable. Of course, only one scene at a time could be shown in the device for it had no reels to handle the band of glass slides.

One evening, early in 1882, Marey had Muybridge present at a large gathering. Helmholtz, Bjerknes, Govi, Crookes and others of the French Academy of Science also were present. The projector fitted with Muybridge's photos of action was given its debut. Marey, years later, commented that those scientists never had seen anything that went so far in the reproduction of nature as Muybridge-type photographs mounted in his Zoopraxinographoscope disk and projector.

In March of 1882 Muybridge was in his native England and presented two showings of his photographs, illustrated with a projector which he called the Zoopraxiscope, borrowing the name almost entirely from Reynaud and the scientific data from Marey. Muybridge gave a lecture, "Attitudes of Animals in Motion, illustrated with the Zoopraxiscope," at a special meeting of the Royal Institution of Great Britain, held on March 13, 1882, with His Royal Highness, the Prince of Wales, honorary member, presiding. The material was previously presented in a paper read before the Royal Society. Muybridge said, "The analyses of some of the movements investigated by the aid of electro-photographic exposures . . . are rendered more perfectly intelligible by the reproduction of the actual motion projection on a screen through the zoopraxiscope."

The walk, trot, amble, rack, canter, run and gallop—which are the several gaits of a horse—were discussed at length with much emphasis on the physiological aspects. Figuratively, Marey must have been standing beside Muybridge as he talked. The lecture, virtually word for word, was given by Muybridge in February, 1833, at the Franklin Institute in Philadelphia. But it is significant to note that then there was no mention of the Zoopraxiscope. Muybridge evidently was not a good operator and there seems to have been difficulty with the projector. Operation of the projector was a problem then because there had to be a relation between the number of pictures and the slits in the projection shutter. Muybridge seems to have found it all too much trouble and turned to the task of taking successive stills which could then be made up into handsome illustrated books.

Meanwhile, Marey in the Spring of 1882 finally finished work on his Photographical Gun which he had conceived several years previously. By this time Marey had a large open air studio set up in the Bois de Boulogne. (Illustrations facing page 121.)

Marey said that he had worked twelve years on the general subject of movement, thereby placing his first efforts back in 1870. The "beautiful instantaneous photographs of Muybridge proved his work," he declared. He continued, saying that in 1878 he had the idea of a photographic gun somewhat analogous to the astronomical revolver of Janssen. Finally, he resolved to devote the Winter of 1882 to the realization of the project.

Marey used his gun to study his favorite project of birds in flight. Marey's photographic gun was the first practical motion picture camera, primitive and limited though it was. In this sense it was the original of all newsreel and other portable motion picture cameras. It is worth noting that in our own time cameras are mounted as "photographic guns" in airplanes as a substitute for gunnery in peacetime and as a check on results during war.

About this time, Georges Demeny (1850-1917) became associated with Marey in this work. Marey always gave credit to his pupil, aide and collaborator. Eventually, however, they parted company because Demeny was interested in commercializing the work and Marey wished to continue with pure science. Later Demeny asserted that his motion picture ideas were superior to Marey's and that he was responsible for the actual execution of all the plans. Demeny at thirteen had begun inventing at his home, but his father, a musician, wanted him to be a university professor. In 1874 he went to Paris and at the Sorbonne was a pupil of Marey in physiology and of Mathias Duval—who also worked with Marey—in anatomy. He did some medical studies and opened one of the first physical education establishments called, *Le Cercle de Gymnastique Rationnelle*. From 1880 on he supervised many of the studies at Marey's Physiological Park.

In July, 1882, Marey proposed the use of a band of sensitized paper in the camera. For various reasons the paper was not satisfac-

tory and, of course, was impractical for direct projection as it might
be set on fire by the projection lamp. The Langenheims of Philadelphia had solved the problem of projecting photographs in the
magic lantern by devising a method of printing the picture on
glass. However, a projector equipped, as the original model of
Uchatius, with a revolving disk could only hold a few glass slides.
This limited the projected pictures to brief action.

In 1887 and 1888 Marey achieved his first real success in what
he called chronophotography, using a box machine which took
eight pictures a second on a single metal plate, or on a sensitized
paper band. Marey had difficulty controlling the paper film because it was not perforated and the pictures were not equally
spaced. This, however, made no difference to Marey since his
main purpose was to obtain data for physiological study, and not
entertainment motion pictures.

In 1888 Marey obtained a successful series of photographs of
fishes swimming, taken with intermittent action on a paper roll
film. The images were taken at the rate of either twenty or sixty
per second. This method of using paper strips obviates the necessity
of operating in a dark camera chamber. At first the paper photographic strips were loaded in a dark room, limiting the scope of the
camera, but later light-proof cameras were perfected. Marey also
proposed an optical system featuring a turning mirror which would
make intermittent action unnecessary. But this method was waste-
ful of film.

A contemporary of Marey and Muybridge, and a skilled photographer in his own right, was Ottomar Anschütz (1846-1907), a
German who worked out one of the best systems for exhibiting a
series of pictures prior to Edison on whom he had an influence.
Shortly after the Muybridge pictures came to Europe, Anschütz
began similar experiments. According to Marey, he achieved better
results than Muybridge, though the results were not perfect, having
a certain amount of distortion. Anschütz obtained sharper photographs of action than Muybridge for his pictures could be used in
the Plateau magic disk or the projector without being copied as
silhouettes as was done with Muybridge's photographs until a
late date.

In 1883 Anschütz tried to use a single camera on the Marey
gun principle but achieved better results with a battery of as many
as forty-eight cameras. The shutter openings in the Zoetrope or

magic disk were modified according to the number of pictures in the particular series.

Anschütz's chief claim to fame rests on the fact that he was the first to combine successfully the instantaneous pictures of an object in motion with the brilliant intermittent flash of the electric Geissler tube. Heinrich Geissler (1814-1879), a German mechanic and physicist, about 1854 invented an electric tube for the purpose of studying discharges in rarefied gases. The apparatus consisted of a thin tube of glass, equipped with platinum wires sealed into each end and filled with a rarefied gas, and an electric battery connection.

In 1889 Anschütz announced the Electrical Tachyscope, a motion picture viewing machine which became popular all over the world. His action photographs were mounted on a wheel and were lighted successively by a Geissler tube's intermittent electric flash. The large photographs were viewed directly by the audience in an adjoining room. Anschütz's device was first depicted in the United States in the *Scientific American* of November 16, 1889. A slot machine model was also devised and was shown at Frankfurt, Germany in 1891, and at the Chicago World's Fair in 1893, where several persons saw it and were given the idea of attempting to achieve projection of life-size motion pictures of complete actions instead of mere phases of motion. (Illustration facing page 149.)

The general technique developed by Anschütz in his Electrical Tachyscope is now used in the taking of stroboscopic motion pictures. It also may be applied in new photographic, motion picture and television processes for increased depth of field.

In 1893 Muybridge lectured at the World's Fair in Chicago at the Zoopraxographical Hall, where hundreds of his pictures were shown. The same material was published by the University of Pennsylvania under the title of *Descriptive Zoopraxography, or the science of animal locomotion made popular.*

Muybridge had settled down in 1885 with a position at the University of Pennsylvania, where he took many pictures with the same battery system, borrowing, however, some ideas about the studio arrangements from Marey. Muybridge never improved his technique or realized that such a cumbersome method could not produce satisfactory results. This did not seem to disturb him for there is no evidence that he sought large screen projection of the magic shadows before audiences.

In February 1886, Muybridge visited Edison at his New Jersey laboratory and showed him plates of successive motion pictures, or, more accurately, a succession of stills of various phases of the same action.

When Muybridge lectured at the London Institution in the Fall of 1889 a complete report was published in the *British Journal of Photography* for December 20, 1889, in an article by W. P. Adams. From this we learn that Muybridge was then using a simple projector fitted with a gear system which revolved before the lens a glass disk of some fifteen inches in diameter on which the photos were mounted; in front of this was a zinc shutter disk with radial slits totalling one more than the number of pictures, in order to give a forward motion to the figures. That was the old Plateau magic disk idea. With the same number of openings in the shutter as pictures, the figures would appear to move their arms and legs and yet stay in the same place; if less shutter openings, there would be an appearance of backward motion. "The disks are rotated at the same speed in opposite directions, and the figures rapidly following each other appear on the screen as a continuous movement of the animal," the English reviewer remarked. Muybridge showed slow and normal action motion. The subjects included a mule kicking, a woman emptying a pail of water, a girl walking down steps carrying a breakfast cup and saucer, and what was said to be the best of all, a little girl finding and picking up a doll. In passing, we may note that in addition to singling out Meissonier for praise, Muybridge asserted that the Japanese were far ahead of everyone else in representing motion in art!

Muybridge eventually retired to his native Kingston, England, after winning fame through his work in America. But he obtained more than fame, for he was able to leave a considerable sum of money, in addition to his instruments, to the local museum. Efforts to locate the Muybridge instruments at the Kingston-on-Thames Museum in 1943 were unsuccessful.

In 1889, Thomas A. Edison, already working on the problem of motion pictures for a year or two, visited the Exposition at Paris and there met Marey who showed him the results obtained with his methods of motion photography, and the reproduction of the scene with a Plateau-disk combined with a projector and the disk illuminated by an electric Geissler tube.

This electrically driven machine, displayed at the exhibit of Fontaine, a French engineer, showed pictures of animals in motion, as well as men and birds. The old photo stand-by of horses in motion in different gaits again was featured. This system rather pleased Marey, as he remarked that it would be hard to construct a better Wheel of Life, though Edison had even then accomplished it in his laboratory at West Orange, New Jersey. The limitations of the method, however, were fully recognized by Marey who mentioned the small number of images which could be shown, the restricted enlargement, and the intermittent movement troubles. Also, the device was noisy and the flicker had not been eliminated.

Thus the year of 1889 brought together two great figures, Marey, a pure scientist whose zeal for learning about locomotion resulted in improvements in what was to be the motion picture art-science, and Edison who invented the first entirely practical motion picture camera and the first film peep-show device which was to be the inspiration for projectors as they were finally established, setting the pattern even to our day.

XV

EDISON'S PEEP-SHOW

‿Edison turns to motion pictures—Donisthorpe of England works it all out on paper—Eastman manufactures film—Edison perfects a motion picture camera, the Kinetograph, and a peephole viewer, the Kinetoscope—World Premiere, New York—April, 1894.

I N THE LABORATORY of Thomas Alva Edison the development of a practicable motion picture camera and viewing apparatus was really achieved. Leadership in the magic shadow art-science came with Edison once again to the United States and it has not left this country since. As a sequel America and motion pictures are linked in the minds of millions throughout the world.

Edison came to the motion picture through his Talking Phonograph, which he had developed not as an entertainment machine but as a device which would be a substitute for the court reporter and in other proceedings requiring exact recording. The motion picture experiments were made rather as a hobby and a diversion from more serious research and invention; the aim was to combine the automatic hearing and speaking of the phonograph with the sight and action of the motion picture.

Curiously enough Plateau, a man who went blind, made the first motion picture possible; Edison who was quite deaf made a great contribution to recording and reproducing sound.

Edison, in November of 1877, sent to his friend Alfred Hopkins, editor of the *Scientific American,* several sketches of models of his new invention in which "speech was capable of indefinite repetition

130

from automatic records." The next month a model was perfected. The incident was described as follows in the December 22, 1877, issue of the *Scientific American:* "Mr. Thomas A. Edison recently came into this office, placed a little machine on our desk, turned the crank, and the machine inquired as to our health, asked how we liked the phonograph, informed us that *it* was well, and bid us a cordial good night." It was noted that the sound was fully audible to a dozen members of the staff who gathered around. The writer also noted, "When it becomes possible to magnify the sound, as it doubtless will, the witness in court will have his own testimony repeated. The testator will repeat his own will."

The editor of the *Scientific American* concluded his comment on the Edison "Talking" phonograph by saying: "It is already possible to throw stereoscopic photographs of people on screens in full view of an audience (i.e., still pictures). Add the talking phonograph to counterfeit their voices and it would be difficult to carry the illusion of real presence much further."

The description of the Edison phonograph attracted wide attention. The article referred to above was quoted fully in *Nature,* a British publication. This led Wordsworth Donisthorpe to set down the first complete plan of the talking motion picture. Others, of course, had had the idea but up to that time the plan had never been expressed so clearly and completely.

Wordsworth Donisthorpe, born in 1847, was an English lawyer who throughout life maintained a lively interest in many affairs. He was an outspoken individualist, being a firm believer in local government. He wrote books on such subjects as *Law in a Free State,* and *Love and Law,* as well as on scientific matters. When he designed his device, the Kinesigraph, he was living at Princes Park, Liverpool.

After reading about Edison's phonograph, Donisthorpe wrote to the *Nature* magazine and referred to the idea of combining the phonograph and still projection suggested by the Editor of the *Scientific American.* Donisthorpe quoted that comment and then said:

> Ingenious as this suggested combination is, I believe I am in a position to cap it. By combining the phonograph and the Kinesigraph I will undertake not only to produce a talking picture of Mr. Gladstone which, with motionless lips and unchanged

expression, shall positively recite his latest anti-Turkish speech in his own voice and tone. Not only this, but the life-size phonograph itself shall move and gesticulate precisely as he did when making the speech, the words and gestures corresponding as in real life. Surely this is an advance upon the conception of the *Scientific American!*

The mode in which I effect this is described in the accompanying provisional specifications, which may be briefly summed up thus: Instantaneous photographs of bodies or groups of bodies in motion are taken at equal short intervals—say quarter or half seconds, the exposure of the plate occupying not more than an eighth of a second. After fixing, the prints from these plates are taken one below the other on a long strip of ribbon or paper. The strip is wound from one cylinder to another so as to cause the several photographs to pass before the eye successively at the same intervals of time as those at which they were taken.

Each picture as is passes the eye is instantaneously lighted up by an electric spark. Thus the picture is made to appear stationary while the people or things in it appear to move as in nature. I need not enter more into detail beyond saying that if the intervals between the presentation of the successive pictures are found to be too short the gaps can be filled up by duplicates or triplicates of each succeeding print. This will not perceptibly alter the general effect.

I think it will be admitted that by this means a drama acted by daylight or magnesium light may be recorded and reacted on the screen or sheet of a magic lantern, and with the assistance of the phonograph the dialogues may be repeated in the very voices of the actors.

When this is actually accomplished the photography of colors will alone be wanting to render the representation absolutely complete and for this we shall not, I trust, have long to wait.

It is not known whether or not Edison read Donisthorpe's suggestion. At any rate, it was ten years, not till 1887, that Edison decided to see about trying to combine the phonograph, greatly improved by this time, and a motion picture apparatus.

After completing improvements on the phonograph in 1886 and awaiting the opening of new laboratory quarters, Edison found himself with some idle moments. Sometime, in the middle or late part of 1887 Edison started work on what was to become his Kinetograph, the first motion picture camera that could photograph a few seconds of action at a time, and the Kinetoscope, the popular peep-show film device which brought the magic shadow art before the modern public and opened the way for the establishment of the motion picture industry.

Edison was assisted in his motion picture experiments by William Kennedy Laurie Dickson, a man who had about the same relation to Edison as George Demeny had with Marey in France. In keeping with the Demeny tradition, Dickson eventually broke with his master and engaged in controversy over priority of ideas and actual contributions to various developments. But Edison and Marey both supplied the ideas and directed the work, while Dickson and Demeny were responsible for carrying out the experiments. Both contributed importantly.

Edison had employed Dickson as a young man, just after he came from England to the United States, and he was a trusted associate, having first been with Edison in the installation of the underground wires in New York City. In 1887 Dickson was called to Edison's private laboratory and given two major projects to supervise: (1) a magnetic device for separating ores, and (2) a device to combine the sounds of the phonograph and pictures.

Late in 1887, in "Room Five" of the Edison Private Laboratory, Dickson started to work on Edison's ideas for a motion picture device. The first efforts were centered on a cylinder recording system, analogous to the cylinder phonograph which Edison preferred to the disk type. He did not bother to patent the disk phonograph style and thereby lost a fortune as he did in other patent matters, including foreign rights to his motion picture camera and peepshow apparatus. The first Edison moving pictures were extremely tiny and had to be inspected through a microscope arrangement. Around 1870 Talbot, the photographic pioneer, in England had done some work on a similar system. The results of Edison's experiments in this connection were not successful.

Next, during 1888 or early 1889, Edison turned to celluloid, made by the Hyatt Company in Newark, and adapted to photographic purposes by Carbutt in Philadelphia. This material was found to be too thick to be rolled conveniently on reels, and did not make a good photographic base. Edison found that notches or perforations were needed to keep the film passing through the camera and viewing device at a uniform rate. He first used notches on the bottom, and finally four perforations on each side for each picture or frame. Edison's arrangement has continued as the work standard.

Edison looked around for a more suitable substance on which to mount the pictures—the age-old need. He found it in film just being manufactured for the first time by George Eastman at Rochester, N. Y. An order was placed and the solution appeared at hand.

For several years Eastman had been seeking a suitable substance for his Kodak cameras in order to make photography simple and foolproof and make widespread amateur use possible. For a time his "roller photography" system used paper rolls coated with a detachable photographic emulsion. This was an improvement over glass plates but the method was cumbersome as the Kodaks had to be returned to Rochester for reloading and processing. Early in 1889 Eastman found the answer in a flexible photographic base —a plastic—and film was born. In August of that year manufacturing began in his Court Street plant in Rochester. The film strips were prepared on glass sheets mounted on 100-foot long tables. Eastman applied for his film patent on December 10, 1889.

When Edison returned from the Paris Exposition of 1889, where Marey had shown him motion picture photographs mounted on a large disk and projected, and also illuminated by an electric flash as in the Tachyscope of Anschütz, Dickson was able to announce success in the motion picture project. That was in October, 1889.

It can never be decided exactly what was shown at the first demonstration, because the interests of Edison and Dickson split and the testimony was contradictory. Nothing was done about it for nearly two years, and the peep-show film machines did not go on public display until the Spring of 1894.

Dickson claimed that the pictures, synchronized with a phonograph, were projected screen size in the Fall of 1889. Edison said there was no projection at the time. Some time between 1889 and 1894, projection experiments were made but Edison did not think screen projection of motion pictures would be commercially successful, believing that a few machines would exhaust the world's demand and once the novelty wore off the business would die. It is also possible that he was not satisfied with the experiments at projection because they must have been quite imperfect. The Edison magic-disk device had continuously running film and a shutter revolving at the rate of ten times a second. No light source then available would give projection with that set-up. Intermittent movement was required for efficient operation in the projector as in the camera.

Harper's Weekly of June 13, 1891, carried a two-page story on the new Edison invention. The device was not claimed to be perfected but one having very wonderful possibilities. The writer said, "To say that the Kinetograph can be nothing more than a marvelous toy would be nasty."

Edison said, "All that I have done is to perfect what has been attempted before, but did not succeed. It's just that one step that I have taken." On August 24, 1891, Edison applied for an American patent but decided not to invest the required sum, approximately $150, to make foreign applications. Too often in the past he found that a patent application by him was simply a form of general advertising to his imitators and competitiors to start using his newest invention.

In 1891 the Kinetograph of Edison was not perfected or highly regarded. In the Engineering News of May 30, 1891, a brief note read:

> The Kinetograph is the latest reported invention of Mr. Thomas Edison. In an interview published in the *New York Sun,* Mr. Edison described this still unperfected machine as an instrument with which he photographs a man or a company of men in action at the rate of 46 per second. The negatives are one-half inch square, taken on a continuous film of gelatine of any length desired. By an ingenious arrangement the images from the gelatine ribbon are later thrown upon a screen and this ribbon is made to move at a rate corresponding to the original rate of action, and at the same time a phonograph is made to repeat the words of the speaker represented. To thus photograph a 30-minute act of an opera, for example, a ribbon 6,400 feet long would be required, each photograph one-half inch square and requiring an inch of linear space.
>
> The commercial sphere of the Kinetograph has not yet been defined.

That last observation was very true for the time being.

In late May of 1891 an indifferent account of the device was cabled to the *London Times* by its New York correspondent. The matter was commented upon in the *Engineering* magazine of London for June 5, 1891. That publication observed that since the time of the invention of the telephone there had been efforts to do for sight what the telephone did for sound. Of Edison's invention of the motion picture camera and viewer it was said, "It is a matter of much less importance and much less originality than thought." It was asserted that it would not be possible to photograph interiors at the rate of 46 pictures per second. But Edison was doing just that in his first motion picture studio.

In the early part of 1893 it was decided to market commercially the peep-show motion picture devices. After a year's postponement, the Chicago World's Fair was scheduled to open in the Spring of 1893 and this was thought an ideal place for the debut of the apparatus. In January of 1893 the famous "Black Maria" Edison Studio was constructed chiefly of tar paper at a cost of about $600, and the first commercial films made. Dickson was producer, director, cameraman and laboratory expert. Fred Ott, a laboratory mechanic, and his sneeze were among the first actors and film "acts." Other subjects included dancers and similar entertainment subjects of a vaudeville character, together with scenic views.

The debut of the projection apparatus had been heralded long before it actually arrived. *The World's Columbian Exposition Illustrated,* published for the Chicago Fair of 1893, said:

> Edison will show his kineto-graph. This machine is a combination, first of the camera and phonograph and then the phonograph and Stereopticon (magic lantern projector). By means of this machine, when a man makes a speech the phonograph takes his words. Connected electrically and in synchronism with the phonograph is a camera which takes pictures of the speaker at the rate of forty-seven per second on a long transparent slip. This is developed and fixed and then placed in a stereopticon which is also in electrical synchronism with the phonograph. The stereopticon shows these photographs on the screen at a rate of forty-seven per second, while the phonograph reproduces the words, and thus a life-like representation of the speaker is given, with his words, actions and gestures precisely as he delivered the speech in the first instance.

EASTMAN and EDISON. George Eastman and Thomas A. Edison, the two greatest American contributors to the practical development of motion pictures, at a meeting in 1928.

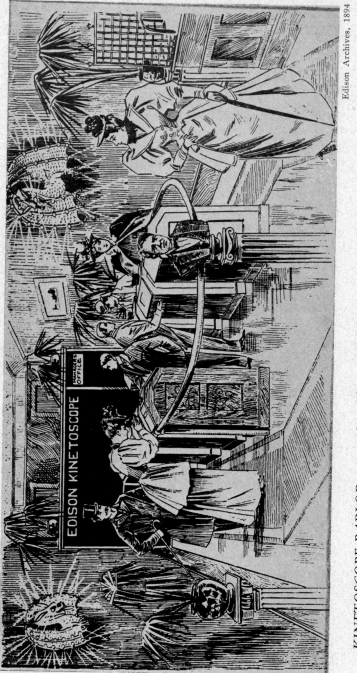

KINETOSCOPE PARLOR, presenting Edison's peep-hole viewer, opened at 1155 Broadway on April 14, 1894. Subsequent showings in London and Paris inspired European inventors.

Edison's projection apparatus was not perfected by the time of
the Fair or indeed for several years afterwards. Even the peep-show
Kinetoscope machines had not been manufactured in sufficient
number for exhibition there. The mechanic on the job was reported to have spent too much time at the local bar instead of
working in the West Orange laboratory. During the Fair Edison's
agents waited for the first shipment of the Kinetoscopes but none
arrived in time.

The patent applications made in 1891 by Edison for "an apparatus for exhibiting photographs of moving objects" and his Kinetograph camera were granted in the Spring of 1893.

The premiere of Edison's Kinetoscope did not take place until
April 14, 1894. That first night was one of the most significant
for magic shadows because out of the Kinetoscope and the Kinetograph camera evolved the modern motion picture devices.

Edison supplied the peep-show Kinetoscope to his agents, Raff
& Gammon at $200 each, and they were retailed to showmen at
prices from $300 to $350. Andrew M. Holland, a Canadian, ac-
quired ten Kinetoscopes and opened up the first Kinetoscope Parlor at 1155 Broadway, New York City. The location previously
was occupied by a shoe store and a half century later it was again
a shoe store. (Illustration on opposite page.)

The Kinetoscopes on Broadway were successful. $120 was
taken in the first night. The original show of films was a kind of
"double feature" in that the spectator was charged 25c to see the
second line of five Kinetoscopes. The films included the famous
"Fred Ott's Sneeze."

In the *Century Magazine* for June, 1894, there was an article
by Dickson and Antonia Dickson on "Edison's Invention of the
Kinetophonograph." Edison wrote a forward which said in part
that he had the idea that it was possible to devise a sight and sound
combination apparatus in 1887. "This idea, the germ of which
came from the little toy called the Zoetrope (i. e., the Plateau-
Stampfer magic disk) and the work by Muybridge, Marie (i. e.,
Marey) and others has now been accomplished, so that every
change of facial expression can be recorded and reproduced life-
size. The Kinetoscope is only a small model illustrating the present
stage of progress but with each succeeding month new possibilities
are brought into view." Edison then prophesied that with his work
and that of others "grand opera can be given at the Metropolitan

Opera House at New York without any material change from the original, and with artists and musicians long since dead."

On June 16, 1894, the *Electrical World* reported on "The Kinetophonograph" and on the nickel-in-the-slot peep-show models on display at the Broadway store. The review was not enthusiastic even then. It concluded: "As to the future of this most ingenious and interesting bit of mechanism, time only will demonstrate whether it is to be a new scientific toy or an invention of real practical value."

Time did demonstrate all that and more.

The reaction to Edison's Kinetograph in Paris, showplace of the world, was much more enthusiastic than in New York. In *La Nature* the wonderful mechanical perfection of the film peepshow apparatus was praised with special note given to the fact that it was driven by electricity. The Werner firm had opened a demonstration of the Kinetoscope at 20 Boulevard Poissonnière, Paris, and the machines were in use all day and every evening.

The Kinetoscope also went on display in Oxford Street, London, in October, 1894, brought there from New York by two Greeks, George Georgiades and George Trajedis. From the showings of the Edison peep-show in New York, Paris, and London, there arose an increased interest in the motion picture. Out of these demonstrations grew projection machines which at last brought the shadow art-science before the world in full development.

XVI

FIRST STEPS

In the United States, England, France and Germany efforts are made to project motion pictures on the screen—Half successes, whole failures, bitter disappointments and yet—perennial hope to harness magic shadows.

DURING THE PERIOD between the time Edison achieved his first success with motion pictures, in 1889, until his peep-show viewing machines were put on public display in New York, Paris and London in 1894, hesitant, unsteady steps, like those of a baby learning to walk, were being taken in advancing the magic shadow art-science.

Progress was made in England under Wordsworth Donisthorpe, an interesting character named Louis Aimé Augustin Le Prince, three associates, Greene, Rudge and Evans, and others. In France, there were Marey and Demeny, with Marey developing what was probably the first real motion picture projector capable of projecting more than one short scene—the limitation of all disk models though it was only intended for laboratory use; and Reynaud with the first popular motion picture theatre which, however, did not use photographic pictures. In Germany, Anschütz, inventor of the Tachyscope, was working on a projector, as were others on both sides of the Atlantic.

Donisthorpe, with the help of W. C. Croft, whom he later described as "a good draughtsman" but not a person skilled in optics, constructed about 1889 a Kinesigraph which Donisthorpe had originally suggested in 1877, at the time he wrote concerning

Edison's phonograph and a plan to combine it with a motion picture machine. Describing the circumstances in a letter to the British *Journal of Photography* of March 12, 1897, Donisthorpe said: "I agreed to give him (Croft) an interest in my invention for drawing and supervising construction of the instrument, as I was at that time busy with other work." He noted that Croft had never claimed to be its inventor. As the reader will recall, Donisthorpe had named his idea, the Kinesigraph, twelve years before this arrangement with Croft.

Donisthorpe and Croft obtained a British patent in 1889 but that expired when not renewed after four years. Donisthorpe complained that an adverse report of some alleged experts killed his plan when he attempted to obtain financing from Sir George Newnes, who might have been the film's first patron. Newnes had made his fortune as a newspaper and magazine owner. He invested a large sum in the Norwegian South Pole expedition of 1898 but was dissuaded from backing motion pictures. Donisthorpe's idea was called "wild, visionary and ridiculous and that the only result of attempting to photograph motion would be an indescribable blur."

"I shall ask in the future," Donisthorpe continued, "to give me all I shall ever get in return for my time and thought, namely, the credit of having been the first to invent, and the first to patent the Kinesigraph, the photography of motion." He also noted that as a barrister he would not care to defend the monopoly of any patentee after 1889. But he was never called upon for that, for in England, as elsewhere, the motion picture patent situation eventually became a hopeless muddle.

In the March 26, 1897 issue of the same publication, the British *Journal of Photography*, Donisthorpe also commented on his Kinesigraph: "The instrument was patented, made and worked before any other saw the light. I do not pretend the results were in all respects satisfactory. What first machine ever is?" Donisthorpe expressed surprise that some had not attempted to copy his machine which operated with a single moving lens and took pictures two and one-half inches in diameter on sensitized paper. This was later made transparent by the application of petroleum jelly or castor oil, a process which Eastman had used, for still pictures, with paper roll film in the United States from 1884 until his film base was developed late in 1889. Donisthorpe held that the continuous action with the moving lens providing the necessary intermittency was a decided advantage over other types: "In one particular, my own invention is so vastly superior even now to all that have come after it, that I am surprised practical men have not adopted it, now that it is open to the English public to do so." As interesting as Donisthorpe's idea was even in 1877 and also in 1889, it is very unlikely that his machine was satisfactory. Even now the intermittent motion picture camera and projector hold practical supremacy except in the case of very high speed photography for scientific purposes.

Louis Aimé Augustin Le Prince (1842-1890), who worked in England, the United States and France, was the son of a French officer who was a friend of Daguerre, the pioneer in photography. Le Prince became a photographer, under the influence of Daguerre and in 1870 went to work in Leeds, Yorkshire, England, where he had his own shop. From shortly after 1880 to 1889 he was in the United States, returning then to Leeds.

Le Prince proposed a multiple-lens camera-projector system. On January 10, 1888 he applied for an American patent, which was issued on November 16 of the same year, on a "Method of an apparatus for producing animated pictures of natural scenery and life." In Le Prince's method, two strips of sensitized paper or other material would be fed alternately through a camera and projector equipped with two sets of rotating lenses. It has been said that Le Prince also had an idea of a system using only one lens.

Years later, at the trial of the American Mutoscope and Biograph Company against Thomas A. Edison, a model of the Le Prince camera-projector was introduced together with results purportedly made by Joe Mason of Biograph, but it was unsatisfactory —the double lens system did not produce evenly spaced pictures and each had to be printed separately. Furthermore, the background had to be treated specially or the figures would appear to jump right and left, because each lens took pictures from a slightly different angle.

Le Prince disappeared in 1890 when he was visiting in France prior to returning to the United States, some investigators have asserted, to show a perfected model of his projector-camera. The mystery of his disappearance has never been solved.

John Arthur Roebuck Rudge, an optician and instrument maker of Bath, England, had developed about 1866 the Bio-Phantoscope, an application of the Plateau magic-disk. He maintained a continuing interest in photography.

About 1882 William Friese Greene (1855-1921), a young man who was a friend of the English photographer Talbot, came into contact with Rudge. In 1885 Greene opened a camera shop in London. A few years later he demonstrated before the Photographic Society a little projection instrument made by Rudge which showed four pictures in rapid succession as, for example, the change of an expression from grave to gay, or a face in the act of blushing. That device was considerably more primitive than the projector first invented by Uchatius, long before Greene was born.

In May of 1890 Rudge showed at a meeting of the Bath Photographic Society a new optical lantern fitted with a mechanism which aimed to represent, by means of a series of photographic slides, men and animals moving as in life. That device, an improvement of the earlier Rudge projector, had one condenser to gather the light and four small projection lenses. Greene suggested the addition of the coloring effects by coating parts of the slides with pigments.

However, the machine was described as unfinished, though in the *Photographic News* of May 30th it was stated, "The effects were, from an entertainment point of view, vastly superior to those produced by Mr. Muybridge and others by the application of the Thaumatrope principle, the unpleasant jerkiness of which is well known." But it was stated that Rudge's machine had several serious defects. The pictures were small and limited to only a few in number. Greene also had a model and gave a demonstration in London which seemed to impress only a Mr. Chang of the Chinese Embassy, one of the invited guests.

The Greene-Rudge or Rudge-Greene machine was partially the work of Mortimer Evans, a civil engineer, with whom Greene made contact in 1889. That year they applied jointly for a patent on a film device. The same year Evans sold out his interest for a reported £1,200 and Greene was in financial troubles.

The Greene-Rudge-Evans device was a box film camera which, it was claimed, could be converted into a projector. By this time celluloid film was available in England as well as in the United States and France. According to the February 28, 1890, *Photographic News,* the camera could take ten photographs a second. The Greene camera, measuring eight by nine by nine-and-a-quarter inches, could take 300 pictures, and a smaller model turned out by Evans, 100 pictures. The reviewer of 1890 wrote, "the object of it is to obtain consecutive pictures of things in motion which can afterwards be rapidly consecutively projected on a screen so as to reproduce, say, a street scene, with the horses, human beings, and other things moving as in nature." Greene this same year claimed that his machine camera would have important military uses. In this he was farsighted, as the modern motion picture camera is an important instrument of military reconnaissance, record and instruction as World War II has so amply demonstrated.

In the British *Journal of Photography* for December 5, 1895, A. T. Story defended Greene's priority of invention and claimed that Greene's projection apparatus of 1889-90 was a success. That conclusion is not inescapable. There appears no concrete evidence that Greene-Rudge-Evans achieved screen projection, for it is obvious that had they done so it would have been widely acclaimed at the time. But they did make a camera and attempted a projector. The camera apparently was practical. Marey and others in France, Anschütz in Germany, Edison, and Wallace Goold Levison in Brooklyn and W. N. Jennings of the U. S. Weather Bureau in Chicago, among others, were making successful motion picture films at that time. Projection remained the great problem.

In 1893 Greene obtained a patent on a device related to the Chronophotographe developed by John Varley, a member of the English landscape painting family. His projection idea included a loop formed by means of intermittent pressure on the film passing before the lens. Greene's November 29, 1893, patent application, accepted exactly one year later, was "to produce by means of reflected light artificial scenery to take the place of the ordinary scenery or background." It included "improvements in apparatus for exhibiting panoramic, dissolving or changing views and in the manufacture of slides for the use thereof." From this it is clear that even as late as 1893 Greene's idea was limited in scope and effectiveness. At this time Greene made some pictures in Hyde Park with a large portable camera.

It was described as a camera and projector in one, but that combination, without many modifications, has never been entirely practical.

Greene had an unhappy, ill-starred life and though not a great inventor deserved better. About 1899 he made attempts at color motion pictures, using a rotating lens with a filter, but here again he was unsuccessful. About 1911 he was brought to the United States to testify in the motion picture patent suit but he did not impress the American attorneys representing Edison's opponents, and he never was called to the witness stand. About 1915 it was reported that he was destitute and Will Day, English motion picture expert, and others, organized a relief fund in his behalf and later he had a minor position with a color photo-engraving firm. At a dinner in his honor in 1921, just after he had once again told the story of his pioneer work on motion pictures, he dropped dead. Apparently his projection efforts were doomed to failure, because they never were based on sound principles. The double lens system has never been made to work satisfactorily.

Marey, who was now using strips of coated celluloid for his instantaneous photographs, sought to devise a suitable projector. This he accomplished in 1893 with what was perhaps the first efficient motion picture projector which could handle more than one brief scene, using long strips of coated celluloid film instead of pictures set on a disk. In order to obtain sufficient illumination, it used sunlight instead of an electric arc or other source of light. This limited Marey's projector to laboratory use, though as late as 1915 some experts claimed that sunlight was better than the electric arc for magic lantern projection.

An available illustration of Marey's projector shows the path of the rays which are reflected from the sun by a heliostat. That device was invented by the Dutch scientist, Willem Jacob, and is simply a mechanically driven reflector which keeps the light of the sun focused on a single spot by compensating for the movement of the earth. In Marey's projector the sun's rays are interrupted by a hand driven shutter wheel and reflected by two mirrors through the film, the light then passing through the projection lens and throwing the pictures onto the screen.

"The motion of the film," Marey wrote, "as it halts at each flash, is brought about by an apparatus not shown in the figure. It is similar to that of the simple chronophotographic apparatus (camera), with the difference that the positive film, having its ends fastened together to make an endless belt, passes over a series of rollers which stretch it taut." This roller system was probably similar to that used by Edison in his peep-show Kinetoscope.

The projector, Marey himself admitted, was not perfect. "The principal imperfection of the chronophotographic projector was a jerkiness due to imperfect equality of the intervals." This resulted from the fact that Marey did not perforate the film because he thought the space along the edge should not be wasted. He knew that Edison had been successful through the use of four perforations on each side of every frame, or picture. He was free to copy this, had he wished, because Edison did not patent the method abroad.

Meanwhile, Marey continued his work and finally, in 1898, announced a successful projector system which overcame his chief difficulty which was the even spacing of the pictures without using the Edison perforations.

His system featured specially constructed rollers which gripped the edges of the film. The next year Marey worked out a combination of the motion picture camera and the microscope, opening the way for much progress in scientific research. He continued to study motion and in 1899 improved his early photographic gun camera so that it would handle about 65 feet of film at one loading. Marey, who was interested only in science and not in commercial exploitation, needed funds which he eventually received from the American Smithsonian Institute, whose secretary, Samuel P. Langley, the aeronautical pioneer, had been following the French physiologist's motion picture studies, including his pioneer work in photographing air currents.

Marey's motto, so far as motion pictures were concerned, was: "It is not the most interesting motion pictures that are the most useful." In this he stood against commercialization, and always for instructional uses.

In 1893 Demeny broke with Marey and patented on October 10, 1893, under his own name, a modification of the Marey camera, which he called the Bioscope. This he was able to do, even though the method had been known at Marey's laboratory, simply because Marey had never actually adopted it. French patents were regularly issued upon application.

Demeny was the motion picture amateur or home-movie-maker's first friend. The instantaneous photographic devices of Marey and others were relatively clumsy and expensive. Demeny brought out a portable camera suitable for amateur use. In operation this model was held over one arm, making it necessary for the cameraman to photograph a scene which he did not see at all, or only imperfectly out of the corner of his eye. Demeny's film was given an intermittent action through two eccentrically mounted pins used as the roll holders. Demeny realized that the pictures must be taken at equal intervals of time and also evenly spaced on the film for successful results. His eccentric camera never actually achieved this result.

In 1891 Demeny became interested in studying speech. In this work he was associated with H. Marischelle, then a young professor at the French national institute for deaf mutes. Marischelle and Demeny had the idea that through photographs of speech the deaf could learn to talk. Demeny developed the Photophone and the Photoscope, which were modified versions of the Marey camera system and a lantern projector equipped with an oxyhydrogen light. Demeny made close-up instantaneous photographs of persons speaking. The phrase, *"Vive la France"* was a popular subject.

Demeny said that the apparatus, "conserves the expression of the face as the voice is preserved in the phonograph." He added that it was, "possible even to join the phonograph to his phonoscope to complete the illusion." That was the idea expressed by Donisthorpe in 1877 and on which Edison had been working since 1887—the combined projector and phonograph or the talking motion picture which indeed was not to be perfected for many decades.

In the Spring of 1892 Demeny tried to exploit commercially the system of Talking Photographs or, more accurately, moving pictures of the action of the mouth in speaking. Demeny always blamed the organization, the *Société Générale du Phonoscope* with which he was associated, for not developing his work. It is probable however, that the Demeny machines were not entirely satisfactory. A few years later, after successful projection of motion pictures had been achieved on a commercial basis, Demeny became associated with Léon Gaumont, and a number of early French machines carried Demeny's name though he alone was not entirely responsible for the design. Demeny and Gaumont developed a projector which included a gear wheel which fitted into perforations on the film and an eccentric pin similar to Marey's camera system.

Anschütz, one of the first successful photographers of motion,

after Muybridge, and the one who introduced the electric Geissler
tube as a method of illumination and projection of a series of
still photos to create the illusion of motion, was continuing his
work in Germany in this period. On November 15, 1894, he obtained a French patent on a "process of projection of images in
stroboscopic movement." This projector had an intermittent light
arrangement and may have been better than Marey's sun model
of 1893, because Anschütz was a professional photographer and
maker of optical instruments while Marey was a professional
physiologist.

In November of 1895 Anschütz showed an improved model of
his projector at the Postal Building in the Artilleriestrasse, Düsseldorf, Germany. A contemporary account in the journal, *Photo-
graphisches Archiv,* published by Dr. Paul E. Liesegang, reported
that the demonstration was "before an invited crowd and was
rightly received with great enthusiasm by all the persons present."
Anschütz had improved his projection apparatus to a point at
which images could be thrown life-size on a screen. Before that
time pictures projected by his *Elektrisch Schnellseher* were only the
size of the original pictures and thus could be seen by only a few
spectators at one time. Anschütz had both motion pictures and
many stills on his program, including scenes taken when the cor-
nerstone of the Reichstag Building was laid. Once again the military connection of magic shadows was shown as Anschütz projected scenes of army life. After the demonstration Colonel A. D.
Tanera stressed the importance of motion picture photography for
the study of military history and also for making observations in
the field.

Reynaud, the first magic shadow showman of modern times and
the immediate forerunner of the motion picture exhibitor of our
day, was now operating his *Théâtre Optique* in Paris. He achieved
the first solid commercial success of the art. From 1892 to 1900,
when the competition of real motion pictures forced him to close,
500,000 persons attended the Reynaud screen entertainments
which were presented every day from three to six in the afternoon
and eight to eleven at night. (Illustration facing page 148.)

The projection apparatus used at the *Théâtre Optique* was a
modification of Reynaud's original Praxinoscope of 1877 and his
simple projector model of 1882. The scenes were painted on transparent celluloid and one magic lantern provided the background

and another optical system which handled the moving film cast the motion effects onto the screen. Rear projection was used with the apparatus concealed on the theatre stage behind the screen. In 1889 Reynaud had obtained a patent on a perforated band of film and he was the first to introduce on a commercially practical basis reels or spools to handle the film. Reynaud was not content to show merely scenes of action but wished to tell a story. Before long it was found that the story film or familiar feature picture was the most popular all over the world.

"Poor Little Peter" (*Pauvre Pierrot*) was one of the most popular of Reynaud's film shows. Harlequin and Colombine were other popular characters. Reynaud provided some of the earliest uses of trick projection, for his apparatus was fully reversible and at times he would create novel and hilarious effects by making the characters jump backwards.

Reynaud stood between the Shadow Plays and pantomimes of the ancients and the modern motion picture. Though he took no part in the development of motion picture photography and its application to the screen, he influenced the art-science by pioneering in the dramatic use of the medium, as well as introducing technical devices which were readily adaptable to motion picture use.

Reynaud was, as Porta two-and-a-half centuries before, a showman. But while he was entertaining the public with screen pictures, the efforts of Marey, Greene, Rudge, Evans, Donisthorpe and many others, including Edison, were preparing the way for the screen art and science of magic shadows. At last the valid motion picture was ready for its public screen debut.

THEATRE OPTIQUE of Emile Reynaud used hand-painted film to tell entertaining stories. The screen plays received wide approval from audiences in Paris.

ELECTRICAL TACHYSCOPE of Ottomar Anschütz was an attraction at the Chicago World's Fair, 1893. It used an intermittent light source.

WORLD PREMIERES

⌐Success at last — Magic shadows reach the screen in living motion — Edison-Armat and the Vitascope—Les Frères Lumière and the Cinématographe —Paul of London and the Animatograph or Theatrograph.

THE MOTION PICTURE made its commercial debut in 1895 and 1896, more or less simultaneously, in Paris, London, New York and elsewhere. That debut is duplicated occasionally at the present time when important Hollywood films have a number of simultaneous "world premieres."

With the introduction of a satisfactory projector of life-size moving pictures which were not limited to a few seconds' duration but could run for a number of minutes, the story of the origin of magic shadow entertainment comes to an end. From that day the phenomenal progress in entertainment and instruction of the motion picture is particularly history of that art-science. Magic shadow history is being written currently every evening on tens of thousands of screens before millions of spectators.

The motion picture projectors which finally were entirely successful and from which the history of the motion picture, properly speaking, arises were all principally based on Edison's Kinetograph film peep-show which in 1894 was shown in New York, Paris and London.

In the Fall of 1894 Louis Lumière saw the Edison Kinetograph demonstrated at the Werner firm exhibit in Paris at 20 Boulevard Poissonière. From this he conceived the idea of combining such an apparatus with the Reynaud-type, which was already providing screen entertainment in Paris. Doubtless, Lumière was also familiar with Marey's work.

Louis Lumière and his brother, Auguste, operated a photographic establishment at Lyons which their father had established. Lyons figured once before in the magic shadow show; it was here that Walgenstein, the Dane, first introduced Kircher's magic lantern in France.

Lumière, who was a successful photographer, decided that the number of images used by Edison per second, forty-eight, was more than necessary so he used sixteen. Lumière, however, borrowed from Edison the idea of perforating the edge of the film, having one on each side of every frame instead of Edison's four. Lumière adopted a claw type intermittent drive for the apparatus which was designed by an engineer, Charles Moissant. Léon Gaumont, who later became associated with Demeny, was Moissant's secretary. The machine was constructed by the Jules Carpentier manufacturing firm.

First experiments were made with coated paper but this was found unsuitable. Celluloid was ordered from the American Celluloid Company and this the Lumières coated themselves because, unlike Edison, they were skilled in photography before they took up the motion picture problem. The Lumières were able to use celluloid but it was not as good as the Eastman motion picture film which Edison had found so satisfactory.

On February 13, 1895, the Lumières obtained a French patent on their camera-projector device, the Cinématographe. The name Cinématographe probably was derived from a French patent issued February 12, 1892, to Léon Bouly who had an idea for a camera which evidently was not reduced to practice.

Le Repas de Bébé, "The Baby's Meal," was the first Lumière film. Other scenes were made in the Lumière photographic plant, together with views of the city, including the Bourse. A demonstration of the apparatus was given there on March 22, 1895, but the Lumières were already established in business and in no haste to develop the new invention. The Cinématographe was shown at Marseilles in April, the month an English patent was obtained, and next shown at the Congress of the National Union of French Photographic Societies, held in June of the same year. There the Lumières created a sensation by filming the delegates arriving for the opening meeting on June 10, developing the film and showing it before the conference was adjourned on June 12. This was the first newsreel use of the motion picture.

On December 28th, the Lumières opened a commercial establishment for the Cinématographe in the Salle au Grand-Café at 14, Boulevard des Capucines. An admission charge of one franc was made, but only a few dozen curious people stopped in the first day. Soon however the fame of the Cinématographe spread throughout Paris. Within a few weeks the Lumière films were playing to "standing room only," averaging more than two thousand admissions per day.

The Lumière Cinématographe was widely hailed. In his usual generous manner, Marey praised the accomplishment even though he must have been disappointed that others had achieved what he had long been seeking. The Cinématographe was shipped to England and the United States at an early date. In New York it was exhibited first in June, 1896, at Keith's 14th Street Theatre, on Union Square. In both countries it was a stimulus to imitators. It continued to be one of the best projectors available for some time. The Lumière claw drive, however, was not as satisfactory as the Maltese-cross type used on some projectors from about 1870 and adopted by Edison for the camera, and it gradually yielded to the newer models.

The Lumières continued to maintain a lively interest in motion picture developments even after their success with the camera and projector. In 1897 they devised a safety condenser as a protection against the fire hazard; in 1898 a peep-show viewing model, and in 1903 they began a study of the possibilities of direct photographing of colors. This research led to a good color process which was later introduced commercially.

In England, Robert William Paul (1869-1943), scientific instrument-maker, who was the son of a London ship owner, was asked by George Georgiades and George Trajedis, two Greeks, to duplicate the Edison Kinetoscope. Georgiades and Trajedis had bought Kinetoscopes in New York from Holland Bros., eastern agents of the first Kinetoscope Company and brought them to London where they were exhibited in October, 1894, at a store in Old Broad Street. Paul inspected the Kinetoscope and knew he could copy it. But he did not believe he was free to do so, feeling sure that Edison had already patented the machine in England. Investigation showed that no such action had been taken. Thereupon at his work shop in Hatton Garden, London, Paul made Kinetoscopes for the two Greek exhibitors and also for himself. With his own machines he opened a display at Earl's Court, London. Soon Paul began work on a camera and projector based on the Kinetoscope peep-show device.

Paul had become interested in creating a machine which would take the spectators into the past or future after reading a fantastic tale of H. G. Wells called *The Time Machine,* publishel in 1894. Paul and Wells talked the matter over, the one a designer and inventor, the other a successful writer gifted with an extravagant imagination. A British patent was applied for but no model or apparatus was ever devised because the money for such an undertaking was not found. The Paul-Wells Time Machine was to be an elaborate affair. Spectators were to be seated on platforms which would move about; adding to the illusion, magic lanterns and motion picture projectors were to flash pictures on all sides. It was another application of the old Phantasmagoria idea to achieve effects by moving the projectors—and in this case, the audience also. Similar effects are achieved with much less trouble, both for the showman and the spectator, in the modern story motion picture.

In the Spring of 1895, Paul made an agreement with Birt Acres by which Acres would make films with a camera constructed by Paul. Previously Paul had been using Edison films but the supply was cut off. His camera was much smaller and more portable than the Edison model. Acres claimed that he had started work on a motion picture camera as far back as 1889 but the effort had not been very successful. By the end of 1893 Acres said he had developed a camera which used one lens or a battery of twelve (Uchatius fashion) and had devoted himself to improving the apparatus instead of "seeking a bubble reputation as a music hall showman," as he himself put it. In 1897 when he had correspondence with Wordsworth Donisthorpe over the latter's early work in motion pictures, Acres was not happy about his motion picture associations, for he said: "Every Tom, Dick and Harry is now claiming to be the inventor and first exhibitor of these animated photographs and I can fully sympathize with Mr. Wordsworth Donisthorpe, inasmuch as some one else has obtained credit for his invention. My own experience with various adventurers is not unique."

Paul's first camera design had an intermittent movement featuring a clamping and unclamping action which was rather hard on the celluloid film made by the Hyatt brothers in Newark, N. J., imported to England and coated for photographic use by the Blair Company. Shortly thereafter, Paul changed to an intermittent movement having a seven-point Maltese Cross. This was an important development.

Paul's projector, called the Animatograph, had its first showing at the Finsbury Technical College on February 20, 1896. Eight days later it was demonstrated at the Royal Institute. Its success came to the attention of a theatreman, Sir Augustus Harris, operator of the Olympia Theatre. A deal was made by Harris with Paul and the projector rechristened the "Theatrograph." After a short but successful run at the Olympia in London, the device was booked for two weeks at the Alhambra, Leicester Square. This motion picture show stayed there four years.

Subjects projected at twenty pictures per second by the Paul device in the early programs were: "A Rough Sea at Dover," a hand colored film; "Bootblack at Work in a London Street," sporting events and many other scenes.

Acres and Paul filmed the Derby of 1896, making some of the first successful topical pictures. Scenes showing the Prince of Wales' horse, Persimmon, winning the Derby were exhibited at the Alhambra the evening after the race, creating a sensation and numerous curtain calls for Paul. The public was amazed.

Paul continued to be interested in motion pictures, especially their scientific aspects, as a kind of hobby, for about 15 years. However, in 1912 he destroyed practically all his films and gave no further attention to the cinema. In addition to his early work in projection and camera design Paul himself had filmed many pictures including a series of animated drawings, à la Walt Disney, to show electrical phenomena resulting from the approach of two magnets. These scientific films were made in association with Professor Silvanus Thompson. Paul also produced a number of comedies and used trick camera work to show motor cars flying to the moon and other bizarre effects. During World War I Paul invented secret war apparatus including an anti-aircraft height finder and anti-submarine device.

Charles Pathé, a great name in the early French film world and carried on by several companies in the United States and elsewhere, bought one of the first Paul motion picture projectors. Previously he had roadshowed the Edison phonograph.

Acres had a projector of his own called the Kinetic Lantern, which he said was finished in January, 1896, but the title was changed to Kineopticon and later to Cinematoscope for a special program for the Prince of Wales. Probably this projector also was made by Paul or he assisted in its design. Acres, however, was primarily interested in his profession of photography, and motion pictures appeared to him to be only one aspect of the subject. In 1897 he said: "There is something in photography and, in particular, in animated photography. Indeed, I think there can be no doubt that animated photography is destined to revolutionize our art-science, both as regards matters historical and scientific, in addition to giving us life-long portraits."

By the time Acres thus spoke the revolution was well under way.

As in France, a number of men immediately started making cameras and projectors in England. The patent rights were confused, chiefly because Edison neglected to secure foreign coverage, leaving the field wide open.

In the United States two factors dominated the experimentation: (1) the Anschütz Electrical Tachyscope, shown at the Chicago Fair in 1893 and (2) the Edison peep-show film device on display in many places, starting in New York in the Spring of 1894.

The projection of life-size motion pictures on a screen before an audience might have been achieved considerably earlier had Edison not felt that there would be no commercial market for such a device. The little peep-show models could be manufactured at rather low cost and sold at a profit, so no impetus was given to the development of a screen projector which might, he thought, quickly dissipate the public's interest and destroy the market. But, it may be recalled, the screen projector, combined with the talking phonograph, had been Edison's original goal when he started the experiments in 1887.

One of the men who was impressed by Anschütz's Electrical Tachyscope at the Chicago Fair was a young Virginian, Thomas Armat. He was a man of means and though associated in a real estate office in Washington, D. C., still had time to follow his scientific interests which induced him to attend the Bliss School of Electricity in Washington. At this time, Armat had already invented a conduit for an electric railway and had refused an offer to in-

terest himself in the distribution of the Edison peep-show film
Kinetoscope. He wanted screen projection.

At the Bliss School Armat was introduced to C. Francis Jenkins,
a young Government clerk, who also was interested in scientific
matters. He had studied the Edison Kinetoscope and, for the Pure
Food Show in Convention Hall, in November of 1894, had shown
a model which instead of Edison's revolving shutter had revolving
electric lights, based on the Uchatius idea. In March of 1894
Jenkins received a patent on a motion picture camera which used
a revolving lens system called the Phantoscope. There is no evidence that Jenkins ever made that camera operate efficiently. It
was described in the *Photographic Times* of July, 1894, as being
only five by five by eight inches in size and weighing ten pounds.
Pictures of an athlete in action, said to have been taken with Jenkins' device were reproduced.

Jenkins was having difficulty achieving projection. Armat and
he decided to form a partnership. Armat was to build a projector
after Jenkins' design and, in return, he would receive rights to the
rotating lens camera patent. The results were a failure. Armat
decided to continue with his own ideas and there was no objection,
as he was supplying the money and the place for the work in the
basement of his real estate office at 1313 "F" Street, in Washington.

Armat decided that the Jenkins idea of continuous movement
with revolving lights was unworkable and chose an intermittent
action. A variation of the Maltese-cross gear system was tried. The
eventual legal dispute between Armat and Jenkins has obscured
data on the system first used. It is certain the results were not
wholly successful.

Three of these machines were built in the Summer of 1895 and
the first showing was held at the Cotton States Exposition at
Atlanta, Georgia, in mid-September. There the chief picture competition was the inspiration—the Anschütz Electrical Tachyscope.
There was also an extensive display of the Edison peep-show
machines. Armat must have been glad to see the Edison activity
because it was from that source that he was getting his film for
the projector.

The projector at the Cotton States Exposition was not well
received. The show finally burned up in a fire that swept the area.
Fifteen hundred dollars was borrowed from Armat's brothers to

continue activities. Jenkins went home to Richmond, Indiana, for his brother's wedding, taking one of the projectors with him.

Meanwhile, Armat hit upon a loop to ease the strain of projection. Jenkins gave a demonstration of the projector on October 29, 1895, and by November 22nd, Armat and Jenkins had disagreed. Jenkins tried to patent some modification on his own, without his partner, but found that he was in interference with the Armat-Jenkins projector patent and signed a concession of priority. From his invention Armat made a great profit which was obtained not without many law suits. Later Jenkins produced a non-intermittent projector of clever but impractical design. He also contributed some original ideas to television development but again the results were not very practical.

Certain other attempts were made to achieve projection of the magic shadows and complete the motion picture system at this time. Most of them also were stimulated by the exhibition of Anschütz's Electrical Tachyscope. One of these was made by Rudolph Melville Hunter (1856-1935), a consulting engineer and inventor of considerable prominence in America. In 1883 Hunter had suggested a Dover-Calais tunnel, something that might have made the Dunkirk evacuation of 1940 much easier; the year before, 1882, he had suggested torpedo boats; later he devised smokeless powder for the French Government and sold some 300 patents to the General Electric and Westinghouse companies. He was also a consultant on acoustics. In his biography, last printed in the 1920-21 edition of *Who's Who* (at which time he evidently retired), Hunter asserted that he "designed and built the first motion picture projector in the world in 1894." His show, scheduled for Atlantic City, never opened. No details are known of his projector.

In the Summer of 1894, two gay young men, Grey and Otway Latham, drug company salesmen operating out of New York, became concessionaires for the Kinetoscope and formed the Kinetoscope Exhibition Company. That firm's chief purpose was to photograph and exhibit prize-fight films. In September of 1894 the young Lathams decided that there never would be much to the peep-show motion picture business and determined to try to get life-size pictures on the screen. They called upon their father, Major Woodville Latham, for assistance.

Major Latham had had a distinguished career as an ordnance officer of the Confederacy during the American Civil War. For a time he was professor of chemistry at the University of West Virginia.

In December, 1894, the Lathams formed the Lambda Company —the Greek "L" for Latham—and a start was made in their quest for a motion picture projector. Dickson was in on the deal although he was still working for Edison. Eugène Lauste, a somewhat secretive friend of Dickson, who was born in Paris in 1857 and had come to the United States in 1887, was the mechanic who worked in Latham's shop. Lauste previously had been employed by Edison.

By the end of the Winter of 1894-95 the Latham project was showing signs of success. A demonstration was held on April 21, 1895, at 35 Frankford Street, New York City and on May 20, 1895, a public showing opened in a small store at 153 Broadway. The Latham projector was found to be inadequate and the following comments were made in the *Photographic Times* for September, 1895: "Even in this, the latest device, there is considerable room for improvement and many drawbacks have yet to be overcome." Specific objections were made to the grain of the film, the fact that it was not entirely transparent, and other factors. It was noted that Major Latham was "persevering" in efforts to improve the device. But some word of encouragement was given: "Even in the present state the results obtained are most interesting and often startling. Quite a crowd of people visit the store at each performance, many making their exit wondering 'How it's done'." It is worth noting that no illustration of the Latham machine was given but instead the Reynaud Optical Theatre of Paris was shown. Latham's projector was called the Pantoptikon and later the Eidoloscope. Latham indignantly denied that parts of his device were borrowed from Edison's machines. It is likely the Major was not aware of all that went on in his work shop.

Dickson eventually joined an organization called the KMCD syndicate, for E. B. Koopman of the Magic Introduction Company; Henry Norton Marvin, a former Edison Associate; Herman Casler, the actual inventor of a camera designed to evade Edison methods, and Dickson. The Casler camera or Mutograph, and the peep-show viewer or Mutoscope, sought to evade the Edison patents, so everything that Edison had they tried to avoid. The Mutoscope in its simplest form was really a step backwards to the old Thaumatrope principle of flashing successive card views before the eye. The Casler camera used unperforated wide gauge film with the pictures irregularly spaced. This made no difference, for the pictures were each mounted on cards.

The Mutoscope and the Mutograph stimulated interest and competition in films, and was the father of the concern around which opposition to Edison centered. The "independents" relied on the American Mutoscope Company, or Biograph as it became, to supply films which would be outside the restriction of the Edison patents. The ensuing patent war was long and bitter but did not materially interfere with the development of the motion picture.

Meanwhile, Edison's agents, Raff & Gammon, were becoming important. The sale of the peep-show Kinetoscopes was only serving to increase the demand for projection and it was feared that the imitators of Edison, such as Lumière, Paul and Latham and others would control the field. Edison, however, was not able— for lack of time or other reasons—to meet the demands of his film agents with perfection enough to satisfy himself. His researches continued but his agents and the public were impatient.

Gammon, of the Raff & Gammon firm, decided to investigate the Armat projector which he had heard about in Washington. A five or six minute show was given on December 8, 1895, by Armat in the basement of his real estate office. In January of 1896 a deal was made whereby Edison would manufacture the projector and it would be introduced under his name, but as "Armat designed." The agents wanted, of course, to play up the name of Edison for commercial reasons. Edison was induced to accept this arrangement by his general manager W. E. Gilmore—who, incidentally, had discharged Dickson.

A demonstration of the Armat-Edison projector was held on April 3 and on April 23, 1896, the Vitascope, as it was called, made its debut at the Koster & Bial's Music Hall on Herald Square, 34th Street, New York City. This was a banner day in the history of the screen. The many hesitant and uncertain steps down through the centuries quickened into an assured march of progress. The public reaction to the Vitascope was excellent, although the programs presented were crude and immature. For several years to come the films offered were only short items which found their chief use as audience "chasers," run as the final number in vaudeville shows. (Illustration facing page 161.)

The *New York Herald* reported on May 3, 1896, that the subjects would soon be lengthened from 50 feet to 150 feet and 500 feet. "Gone With the Wind," the mammoth of 1941, was 20,000 feet long. New attractions promised in the first days were to include Niagara Falls, which Langenheim had photographed with marked success a half-century earlier; a steamer going down the Lachine Rapids, and an ocean liner leaving its dock.

The *Herald* said: "The result is intensely interesting and pleasing but Mr. Edison is not quite satisfied yet. He wants now to improve the phonograph so that it will record double the amount of sound it does at present, and he hopes then to combine this improved phonograph with the Vitascope so as to make it possible for an audience to witness a photographic reproduction of an opera or a play—to see the movements of the actors and hear their voices as plainly as though they were witnessing the original production itself."

The "world premiere" newspaper review concluded: "And when it is remembered what marvels Edison has produced, it would not seem at all improbable that he may yet add this one to his many others."

The talking picture, however, did not make its real debut for three decades.

The *New York Tribune* on Sunday, May 3, 1896, said: "Edison's Vitascope has made a decided hit at Koster & Bial's Music Hall. Tomorrow evening all the pictures will be in colors. The Vitascope, together with Albert Chevalier, is drawing large audiences."

Raff & Gammon now had something that could be sold easily; the Vitascope was everywhere well received. Eighty projectors of the Armat design were delivered by the Edison company from April to November of 1896. And Edison started renewed work on his own "Projecting Kinetoscope," independently of Armat.

An advertising brochure for the Vitascope told the story this way:

Several years ago Mr. Edison conceived the idea of projecting moving figures and scenes upon a canvas or screen, before an audience.

Owing to the pressure of his extensive business, he could not fully develop his inventive ideas at the time. However, he put his experts to work upon a machine which should reproduce moving pictures upon a small scale, and the Kinetoscope was the result.

After perfecting the Kinetoscope, Mr. Edison turned his attention to his original plan of inventing a machine capable of showing the moving figures and scenes, life-size, before a large audience. His ideas soon took practical form, and as long ago as last Summer a very creditable result was obtained; but Mr. Edison was unwilling to give his unqualified approval until the highest practicable success had been achieved. Since then, Mr. Edison's experts have been putting his ideas and suggestions to practical test and execution and, in addition, some of the original ideas and inventive skill of Mr. Thomas Armat (the rising inventor, of Washington, D. C.) have been embodied in the Vitascope; the final result being that today it can almost be said that the impossible had been accomplished, and a machine has been constructed which transforms dead pictures into living moving realities.

On the last page of the advertising brochure for the Vitascope it was asserted that the rights were controlled for the world. If that had been true the Edison firm would have reaped an incalculable fortune. But by this time many projection machines and cameras by diverse manufacturers were coming into use in many countries.

Magic shadows—living reproductions of people and the world —at last had reached the screen.

*

But there still remained a long and important step to be taken in order that the true fidelity of living pictures could be achieved. Sound needed to be added to sight. So again, thirty years later, magic shadow history was made—this time at the Winter Garden theatre in New York City, on October 6, 1927. The event was the premiere of "The Jazz Singer," starring Al Jolson and presenting the Vitaphone system of talking motion pictures. This rounding out of the faculties of magic shadows came through the enterprise of the Warner brothers—Harry, Sam, Albert and Jack—and the technological achievements of Dr. Lee DeForest, Theodore Case, Charles A. Hoxie and the others who gave the screen its voice.

Generally, the motion picture industry was skeptical of talking motion pictures and their future. But soon public opinion registered emphatically and the addition of sound was accepted as an indis-

ROBERT W. PAUL, instrument maker, constructed cameras and projectors in England.

LOUIS LUMIERE, inventor of the Cinématographe camera and projection system.

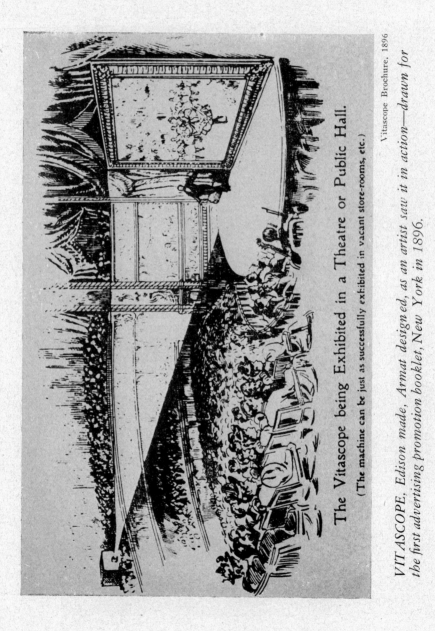

Vitascope Brochure, 1896

The Vitascope being Exhibited in a Theatre or Public Hall.

(The machine can be just as successfully exhibited in vacant store-rooms, etc.)

VITASCOPE, Edison made, Armat designed, as an artist saw it in action—drawn for the first advertising promotion booklet, New York in 1896.

pensable faculty of the medium of the screen. And now finally the ancient and persevering urge for true living pictures was satisfied.

*

And thus the motion picture, like many another achievement of the human heart and hand and mind, has come down to us as the result of incalculable effort on the part of many. This great benefaction to humanity the world over is the realization of the aspirations of many who labored unceasingly and well down through the centuries—Archimedes, Aristotle, Alhazen, Roger Bacon, Leonardo da Vinci, Porta, Athanasius Kircher, Musschenbroek, Paris, Plateau, Uchatius, Langenheim, Marey, Muybridge, Edison and others. It is the creation of men of many centuries and many nations and from these diversities of time and persons it has gained its amazing power, its universal appeal.

THE END

Appendix I

MAGIC SHADOWS

A Descriptive Chronology

B. C.

? First artist's aspiration to recreate life and the movement of the world of nature.

6000 to 1500 Babylonians and Egyptians acquire first scientific knowledge of the light and shadow art-science. Crude magnifying glasses are fashioned. Light and shadow are used for entertainment and deception.

Chinese Shadow Plays make use of silhouette figures cast on a screen of smoke.

Japanese and English mirrors are devices for reflecting strange optical illusions.

340 Aristotle gives impetus to all studies. First recorded magic shadow experiment—"the square hole and round sun."

Euclid demonstrates that light travels in straight lines, a fundamental for all projection and photography.

225 Archimedes devises the famous "Burning Glasses" for destroying ships of the enemy, which may or may not have been a factor in the defense of Syracuse.

60 Lucretius, the Roman poet, writes *De Rerum Natura,* "On the Nature of Things," combining verse and philosophy and a bit of science. The work contains a reference erroneously interpreted as a description of a magic lantern show.

A. D.

50 Pliny and Seneca advance scientific knowledge. The effect of the atmosphere on silver is noted by Pliny. Seneca writes on the persistence of the sensation of vision.

163

79 Pompeii and Herculaneum are destroyed by the eruption of Vesuvius. Excavations have recovered a lens and a sound effects system probably used by the priests to trick the people.

130 Ptolemy writes the *Almagest* which was the standard work on optics for centuries. Subjects treated included the persistence of vision, the laws of reflection and studies of refraction.

170 Galen, an early medical authority, considers the problems of vision, fundamental to the scientific application of light to create the illusion of motion.

510 Boethius tries to measure the speed of light. Charges of treason and magic result in his decapitation in 525 at the order of his former patron, King Theodoric, Ostrogoth dictator of Italy.

750 Geber, Arabian alchemist, notes the effect of light on silver nitrate, a basis of photography.

870 Alkindi, an Arab, advances scientific learning, including work in the fields of astronomy and navigation.

1010 Alhazen, greatest of the Arab scientists in optics, advances the art-science of magic shadows and succeeds Ptolemy as the standard authority.

1020 Avicenna, another Arab, studies the movements of the eye in vision.

1175 Averroës, famed Arab philosopher, studies vision and eye movement.

1267 Roger Bacon, English Friar, describes the use of mirrors and lenses and attacks necromancers who use such devices to deceive the people.

1270 Witelo, a Pole called Thuringopolonus, writes on all phases of optics and with Bacon dominates experiments in this field for generations.

1275 St. Albertus Magnus, Dominican scholar and teacher of St. Thomas Aquinas, takes special interest in the rainbow and assigned a finite but very great velocity to light.

1279 John Peckham, English Franciscan and alchemist, in his *Perspectiva Communis* points out that the rays of the sun can be shown in any desired place, indicating a knowledge of the "dark room."

1300 Spectacles are introduced in Italy.

1438 Gutenberg develops printing from movable type which hastens the exchange of all knowledge, an aid to the growing interest in all light and shadow problems.

1450 Leone Battista Alberti, an Italian cleric and architect, designs the *camera lucida,* a light and shadow device similar to a large box camera for the use of artists in copying, drawing and nature.

1464 Nicholas of Cusa writes the first book about eye glasses.

1500 Leonardo da Vinci sets down the first accurate description of the portable or "dark room" *camera obscura* and shows its relation to the human eye.

1520 Francesco Maurolico, a mathematician and astronomer of Messina, develops the scientific but not experimental principles of light as reflected by mirrors and the use of light theatres. The next year he describes the construction of a compound miscroscope.

1521 Cesare Cesariano, an architect and writer on art, asserts in his introduction to a new edition of Vitruvius that a Benedictine monk, Don Papnutio or Panuce, constructed a satisfactory *camera obscura.* Construction details are given for the first time in a published work.

1540 Erasmus Reinhold uses a *camera obscura* to observe an eclipse of the sun at Wittenberg. Ancient astronomers had found it impossible to observe an eclipse unless there were clouds in the sky or the sun was near the horizon to cut down the light.

1550 Girolamo Cardano, an Italian physician and mathematician, describes how the box *camera obscura* can be used for entertainment purposes.

1558   Giovanni Battista della Porta of Naples writes of making many light and shadow devices and earns the right to the title, "first screen showman."

1568   Monsignor Daniello Barbaro introduces the projection lens in the *camera obscura.*

1585   Giovanni Battista Benedetti, a patrician of Venice, publishes the first complete and clear description of the *camera obscura* or box camera equipped with a lens.

1589   Porta's book, *Natural Magic,* reprinted with a new section on the use of the *camera obscura* for entertainment purposes.

1604   Johannes Kepler explains the use of the "dark chamber" device for astronomical work.

1612   Christopher Scheiner, a German priest, uses the device to study sun spots.

1613   François d'Aguilon, another priest, stimulates the study of all branches of optics and is the first to coin the name "stereoscopic."

1620   Sir Henry Wotton, diplomat and author, gives one of the first descriptions in English of the *camera obscura* for drawing purposes. He describes a portable tent camera.

1626   Willebrord Snell promulgates his "law" on the angles of reflection and refraction, essential data for grinding and polishing lenses and other phases of advanced optics.

1644
or   Athanasius Kircher invents the magic lantern at Rome.
1645   This is the first projector of magic shadows.

1646   Kircher's book, *Ars Magna Lucis et Umbrae,* "The Great Art of Light and Shadow," is published.

1652   Jean Pierre Niceron shows how irregular figures can be made into plain figures through a mirror projection lens system.

1658   Gaspar Schott develops Kircher's projection lantern in his *Wonders of Universal Nature and Art.*

1665   Walgenstein, a Dane, shows a Kircher-type magic lantern in France and elsewhere.

1669   Robert Boyle furthers interest in magic shadows with a description of a "Portable Darkened Room" in his *Systematic or Cosmical Qualities of Things.*

1671   The second edition of Kircher's *Ars Magna Lucis et Umbrae* is published with an expanded treatment of the magic lantern and specific instructions on how it may be used for entertainment and instruction.

1674   Claude Milliet de Chales, a Frenchman, describes the use of an improved projection lens system for the magic lantern.

1680   Robert Hooke develops his *camera lucida* in England. His plan was suggested in 1668 but by 1680 it had been improved and showed images in a room which was only partially darkened.

1685   Johann Zahn develops Kircher's lantern to its highest state prior to the introduction of improved light sources of electricity or gas in the 19th century.

1692   William Molyneux, of Dublin, in his *Dioptrica Nova* introduces the improved magic lantern, scientifically described, in the British Isles.

1704   John Harris, divine and scientific writer, describes a better camera fitted with a "scioptic ball" or perforated globe of wood which could be turned in different directions to show diverse views.

1711   Willem Jakob Van 's Gravesande, a Dutchman, discusses projection and is credited with inventing the heliostat which made it possible for scientists to use the light of the sun in projection work, as well as in astronomy.

1727   Publication of the revised *Dictionnaire Universel* of Abbé Antoine Furetière edited by M. Brutel de la Rivière—with a description of the magic lantern spreads the use of the projector in France.

Johann Heinrich Schultze, a German professor of eloquence and antiquities, observes that light has an effect on a bottle of chalk and silver nitrate solution. He explains how others can duplicate his effects by concentrating the sun's rays on a bottle of the solution by means of a burning glass.

1736   Pieter van Musschenbroek introduces "motion" into the magic lantern by using a multiple slide system and a mechanical means of shaking one of the glass slides.

1747   Leonhard Euler, a Swiss mathematician, describes a camera for Empress Catherine of Russia.

1752   Benjamin Franklin, pioneer American scientist, writes: "I must own I am much in the dark about light."

1753   Three different types of the camera in fixed and portable models are described in the famous French *Encyclopédie*.

1760   Abbé Nollet's "Whirling Top," a toy which shows the illusion of motion in a striking fashion, is a popular children's plaything in Paris.

1772   François Séraphin, a magician, is credited with introducing the art of shadow plays in France.

1777   Carl William Scheele, a Swedish chemist, discusses the action of light on silver chloride.

1780   Jacques Alexandre César Charles, working under the patronage of Louis VXI at the Louvre, invents the Magascope or a projection microscope. This was a development of an earlier device he had for throwing on a screen images of living persons.

1790   Pierre L. Guinard, a Swiss glass worker, makes improvements in the processes of grinding and polishing optical glass.

1798   Etienne Gaspard Robertson resurrects "ghosts" of the French Revolution with his Phantasmagoria shows, featuring a magic lantern mounted on wheels and a screen of smoke.

1802   Tom Wedgwood repeats the experiments of Schultze and Scheele and announces a process of copying paintings on glass and making profiles by the action of light upon nitrate of silver.

1807   Dr. William Hyde Wollaston invents a new model of the *camera lucida*.

1814   Joseph Nicéphore Niepce begins work on photography.

1815   David Brewster, Scottish scientist, invents the Kaleidoscope, an optical device which creates colorful designs.

1820
to   English and French scientists study the optical phenomena
1825   arising from the rotation of wheels.

1820   "J. M.", anonymous English scientist, comments on wheel phenomena in the English *Quarterly Journal*, stimulating study of a basic factor in motion picture photography and projection.

1824   Peter Mark Roget, of *Thesaurus* fame, discusses wheel phenomena and gives an explanation—an early scientific account of the "persistence of vision" with regard to moving objects.

1825   William Ritchie, rector of Tain Academy, England, develops an improved lantern for "ghost" projection using a gas light source.

1826   John Ayrton Paris' Thaumatrope, or small disk with part of the complete scene on one side and part on the other side, becomes a scientific plaything. (Charles Babbage, English scientist and mathematician, claims an earlier invention on the same lines. The invention of the Thaumatrope has also been attributed to Sir John Herschel, Dr. William Fitton and Dr. William Hyde Wollaston.)

1827   Niepce's Heliotypes, which were photo silhouettes obtained after as much as six or twelve hours' exposure, are shown in London.

1827   Sir Charles Wheatstone invents the Kaleidophone, or Phonetic Kaleidoscope, to illustrate "amusing acoustical and optical phenomena."

1828   Joseph Antoine Ferdinand Plateau, a Belgian, makes the first motion picture machine—a device which changes a distorted drawing into a correct and natural one.

1829   Niepce and Louis Jacques Mandé Daguerre, a painter and showman, form a partnership for the development of photography.

1830   Michael Faraday takes up the study of wheels and spokes and motion, and the effects of motion on the human eye.

1832   Plateau and Simon Ritter von Stampfer, Austrian, independently introduce the magic disks which show real motion. These spinning wheels with a series of designs are called the Fantascope, Phénakisticope or Stroboscope.

1834   William George Horner in England devises an improved model of the magic disks by arranging the designs on a horizontal instead of vertical wheel. This made it possible for several persons, instead of one, to see the movement at the same time.

Ebenezer Strong Snell, a professor at Amherst, introduces the picture disks in the United States.

1835   William Henry Fox Talbot begins his photographic investigations.

1838   Wheatstone invents the Stereoscope which gives the illusion of depth by presenting two slightly dissimilar pictures to the two eyes.

Abbé François Napoléon Marie Moigno, in France, uses magic lanterns made by François Soleil, Parisian optician and father-in-law of Jules Duboscq, to illustrate chemical reactions.

1839   Talbot in England and Daguerre in France announce practical photographic systems which make it possible to permanently record the age-old images of the "dark room" or *camera obscura*. Hippolyte Bayard experiments with paper photographic prints.

1845   Johann Müller in Germany uses the Fantascope disks to study the wave motion of light. Similar work is carried out by others.

1848 E. M. Clarke demonstrates, at the London Polytechnic Institution, a good magic lantern fitted with an oxygen-hydrogen lamp. He publishes a booklet on lantern projection—"Directions for using the philosophical apparatus in private research and public exhibition."

1849 Brewster introduces a binocular camera for photographing stereoscopic pictures. It is copied in Paris by M. Quinet, a photographer, who calls it the Quinetoscope.

1850 Frederic and William Langenheim, of Philadelphia, patent the Hyalotype, a process for making positives on glass slides suitable for use in the magic lantern. This makes it possible to combine photography and the Plateau-Stampfer disks.

Wheatstone shows in Paris an improved stereoscope which uses photos specially made for it.

1852 Photographs instead of drawings are used in the magic disks by a number of scientists and photographers, including Wheatstone, Jules Duboscq in Paris, Antoine François Jean Claudet. The imperfect photographic equipment as well as the limits of the individual disks resulted in unnatural moving pictures.

1853 Franz von Uchatius, an Austrian army officer, develops a motion picture projector which combines the Plateau-Stampfer disks and the magic lantern of Kircher.

1854 Sequin, a Frenchman, obtains a patent on an improved projector.

1860 to 1865 Claudet, Duboscq, Shaw and others experiment with the magic disk and the stereoscope in an effort to combine the illusion of motion and the illusion of depth.

1860 Thomas Hooman Dumont draws up on paper a motion picture camera. Other attempts are also made but the apparatus is not yet ready.

Pierre Hubert Desvignes obtains a French patent on a system which suggests the use of an endless band and an apparatus for looking at stereoscopic views and small objects in motion. He also used models instead of designs or photographs in his efforts to recapture motion.

1861   William Thomas Shaw announces the Stereostrope which mounted eight stereoscopic pictures on an octagonal drum. These were viewed in an ordinary Wheatstone Stereoscope. "The effect of solidarity is superadded so that the object is perceived as if in motion and with an appearance of relief as in nature."

Coleman Sellers in the United States patents the Kinematoscope which is a toy using a paddle wheel action to show "posed" motion pictures.

1864   Louis Ducos du Hauron patents a motion picture photography-projection system, but there are no adequate materials available to make it practical.

1865   James Laing announces the Motorscope—another solid-plus-motion device akin to that of Shaw.

About this time the following also showed similar devices: Léon Foucauld, French astronomer, the Stereofantascope or Bioscope; Cook and Bonelli, the Photobioscope; Humbert de Moland, Keville, Almeida, Seely and Lee.

A. Molteni, optician, of Paris, invents the Choreutoscope Tournant which uses a Maltese Cross movement, a type which was of considerable importance in the development of intermittent movement in projectors.

1866   Lionel Smith Beale, a specialist in the use of the microscope, perfects the Molteni turning wheel.

1868   John Wesley Hyatt of New York invents celluloid while seeking a substitute for ivory for billiard balls. (Prior to this time Alexander Parkes in England worked on a product somewhat similar to celluloid but the process was different.)

Langlois and Angiers patent an improved Thaumatrope which uses miscroscope views seen through a lens system.

Linnett develops the Kineograph or little book which, when thumbed rapidly, flashes successive pictures before the eye, creating an illusion of motion.

1869   O. B. Brown obtains the first U. S. patent on a projector— it is the old familiar model of Uchatius and uses hand-drawn designs.

James Clerk Maxwell, famed for his work in color and electricity, develops what is hailed as the perfect Zoetrope or Wheel of Life by substituting concave lenses for the slots in order to eliminate distortion. Hand drawn figures were projected in a similar system.

1870   Henry Renno Heyl, of Philadelphia; Bourbouze, French scientist; Sequin, a printer and artist, and others combine "posed" motion pictures with the magic lantern so that flickering, brief and imperfect moving images appear on the screen. Bourbouze uses pictures at the Sorbonne University to show the actions of pistons, vapor and air machines.

1872   Eadweard Muybridge or Edward James Muggeridge and others make progress on the road to the photographing of successive still pictures of objects in motion.

Lionel Smith Beale, in England, despairs of obtaining enough light by ordinary methods so he cuts his images on a thin brass rim and uses a primitive intermittent movement and shutter in projection. Device was called the Choreutoscope.

1874   Pierre Jules César Janssen, French astronomer, perfects the photographic-revolver, a fixed-motion picture camera, to photograph the transit of Venus in Japan.

1875   Caspar W. Briggs, successor to the Langenheims in Philadelphia, brings out a projector.

1877   Thomas A. Edison invents the Talking Phonograph. Wordsworth Donisthorpe, an English lawyer, suggests the Kinesigraph to combine the effects of the phonograph and the magic lantern.

Charles Emile Reynaud develops the Praxinoscope, an ingenious arrangement of the Plateau-Stampfer magic disks, using a mirror set in the center.

1878   Muybridge and John D. Isaacs, an engineer, achieve photographic success with a "battery" of still cameras hooked up to take successive pictures of moving objects.

Etienne Jules Marey, physiologist, in Paris analyzes the motion pictures made by the Muybridge-Isaacs system by means of the magic disks.

1879 Reynaud works out a projection model of his Praxinoscope.

1881 Jean Meissonier, French painter, uses a magic disk device with photos to analyze motion and assist him in his work.

1882 Muybridge, guided by Marey in Paris, mounts his photographs on a Uchatius magic lantern and actual motion pictures briefly are thrown on the screen before an audience with the Zoopraxiscope.

Reynaud has a projector called the Lamposcope—as all early projectors, limited to showing the one scene made up of a set of stills mounted on the edge of a disk.

1884 George Eastman begins at Rochester, New York, the manufacture of roll paper film for use in his Kodak camera.

1887 Hannibal Williston Goodwin, an Episcopalian minister, obtains a patent on Photographic Pellicle which is described as transparent, sensitive and like celluloid. His efforts came after becoming interested in photography through magic lantern entertainments he conducted for his congregation. His patents ultimately led to the business of Anthony & Scoville, now known as Ansco.

Marey, in France, achieves first success with his chronophotographic or motion picture system using slips of coated paper film.

Edison begins experiments aimed at producing an apparatus which would do for sight what the phonograph had done for sound—i. e., motion pictures; and a device which would combine both—i. e., a sound motion picture system.

1888 John Carbutt achieves success in his efforts, started several years before, to treat with photographic chemicals long strips of celluloid obtained from the Hyatt Company.

Eastman continues work which lead to successful motion picture film.

Louis Aimé Augustin Le Prince patents a multiple lens camera-projector system which, however, never produced satisfactory results.

1889 Ottomar Anschütz stimulates interest in motion pictures with his Electrical Tachyscope—a good viewing apparatus for a series of pictures successively illuminated by a Geissler tube. This device was the progenitor of modern strobo-scopic photography.

Edison and Kennedy Laurie Dickson, his assistant for motion picture research, continue investigations. Film stock is ordered from Eastman. First successes are claimed. In Paris, Marey shows Edison a magic disk equipped with photos and lighted by electric flashes.

Eastman applies, on December 10, 1889, for a patent on "the manufacture of flexible photographic films." The patent was not issued until 1898 and a long legal battle ensued with the Goodwin estate until a compromise was reached.

1889
to
1894 Edison investigations aimed at producing a motion picture camera and projector continue.

1889 Wordsworth Donisthorpe and Croft obtain the first real motion picture patents in England but never had sufficient financial backing to perfect the system or even make an efficient model.

1890 John Arthur Roebuck Rudge and William Friese Greene and Mortimer Evans, in England, construct a simple, limited motion projector.

1891 Edison's Kinetograph camera and Kinetoscope viewing apparatus completed and the patent application made. The patent was not issued for two years.

1892 Reynaud runs the Théâtre Optique in Paris, the first film theatre which uses hand-drawn and not photographed pictures.

1893 Marey develops a motion picture projector which uses the sun for its light source.

Greene patents a camera and projector system which is limited in scope.

1894 Edison peep-show Kinetoscopes go on display on April 14th, at 1155 Broadway, New York, and later that year on Oxford Street, London, and in Paris. These demonstrations influence a number of scientists and photographers who finally solved the problem of screen projection of continuous motion pictures.

Anschütz patents an early projection model in France.

Demeny uses a camera and projector system somewhat similar to that developed under Marey.

1895   Successful projection of motion pictures onto a screen achieved by Louis and Auguste Lumière with the Cinématographe, in France; by Robert W. Paul with films made by Birt Acres in the Bioscope, in England; by Thomas Armat, C. Francis Jenkins, the Lathams, and others in the United States.

1896   Screen projection of motion pictures becomes a commercial reality and the magic shadow art starts on the way to becoming the greatest entertainment medium ever known. In New York the premiere is held at Koster & Bial's Music Hall, Herald Square, New York City, on the evening of April 23, 1896.

In addition to those named, the following, among many, were also working on screen projection in the 1895-96-97 period of success: Georges Melies, who brought the spirit of Phantasmagoria to the modern motion picture; Max Skladanowski, who claimed a projection show at the Wintergarten in Düsseldorf in the Fall of 1896; Owen A. Eames, of Boston; Edwin Hill Amet, of Chicago; Henri Joly, W. C. Hughes, Cecil M. Hopwood, Carpentier, Drumont, Werner, Gossart, Auguste Baron, Grey, Proszynski, Bets, Pierre Victor Continsouza, Raoul Grimoin-Sanson; Perret & Lacroix; Ambrose Francis Parnaland, Sallé & Mazo; Pipon; Zion, Avias & Hoffman, Brun, Gauthier, Mendel, Messager, Cheri-Rousseau, Mortier, Wattson, Maguire & Baucus, Phillip Wolff, F. Brown, F. Howard, Ottway, Rowe, Dom-Martin, Appleton, Baxter & Wray, Riley, Prestwich, Newman & Guardia, Rider de Bedts, Noakes & Norman, Clement & Gilmer, etc., etc.

Thus the chronology of magic shadows, or the origin of the motion picture, concludes with a roll of names of men of many nations, a point illustrative both of the universal appeal of the motion picture and of the long and diverse collection of individuals who contributed to the development of the art-science.

Appendix II

BIBLIOGRAPHY
and Acknowledgements

THE PURSUIT of the story of the origin of the motion picture has been carried on intermittently since the Winter of 1936-37. As historical books must be, it is based mainly on the written record. Efforts were made, whenever possible, to go directly to the source material. The whole field of books on the motion picture, as well as standard biographical and scientific works, was surveyed.

Research was conducted principally at the following libraries: Library of Congress, Georgetown University, Surgeon General's, in Washington, D. C., New York Public and Columbia University in New York City. Work was also done at the Academy of Motion Picture Arts and Sciences, Hollywood; New York Engineering Societies, the British Museum, London; Trinity College, Dublin, and Vittorio Emanuele—formerly Collegio Romano—library, Rome. Part of the original Kircher Museum at Rome, was inspected in the Summer of 1939. (The early projector models, according to the evidence now available were destroyed shortly after Kircher's death.) The 1939 exhibit of the works of Leonardo da Vinci in Milan was visited.

Terry Ramsaye, author of *A Million and One Nights—A History of the Motion Picture,* and editor of *Motion Picture Herald,* is responsible for suggesting lines of study which led to the decision to write this book. Also, he has rendered valuable guidance and assistance especially in connection with the early American motion picture pioneers, and in reading the manuscript and contributing the foreword.

Special thanks are due to members of the faculty of Georgetown University for making available works in the Riggs Memorial Library of that institution and giving assistance on special aspects of the subject. The writer likewise is grateful for having had the opportunity of consulting books in the splendid Epstein Photographic Collection at the Columbia University Library, and for biographical notes on Robert W. Paul secured through the Cambridge Instrument Company. Appreciation is expressed to Rev. Hunter Guthrie, S.J., dean of the Graduate School, Georgetown University, and to Dr. Alfred N. Goldsmith, consulting engineer, for kindness in reading proofs and offering invaluable suggestions.

BIBLIOGRAPHY

The following is a list of books, arranged according to the chapters of this story, which may serve to disclose any particular part of the subject to readers who wish to make a detailed study. In general articles in the various periodicals give the first, and often most complete, publication of each development. This list represents only a limited number of the books and publications consulted, but the principal titles are included:

GENERAL

TERRY RAMSAYE. *A Million and One Nights.*
New York, 1926.
> A standard history of the motion picture and a special source of material on Edison, Muybridge, Armat, Latham and other early American experimenters.

JOSEPH ANTOINE FERDINAND PLATEAU.. "Bibliographie des principaux phénomenes subjectifs de la vision depuis les temps ancients jusqu'à la fin du XVIII siècle," *Mémoires.* Académie Royale des Sciences, des Lettres et des Beaux Arts de Belgique. Brussels, 1877-1878.
> A most complete, annotated list of works on vision.

LYNN THORNDIKE. *History of Magic and Experimental Sciences.*
New York, 1923-41.
> A monumental reference work of particular interest to scholars.

HENRY V. HOPWOOD. *Living Pictures:* their history, photo-reproduction and practical working. London, 1899.

ROBERT BRUCE FOSTER. *Hopwood's Living Pictures.*
London, 1915.
> The original edition of this book and the revised edition both include a general review of early activity plus a valuable bibliography of the period from 1825 to 1898.

G. MICHEL COISSAC. *Histoire du Cinématographe* de ses origines jusqu'à nos jours. Paris, 1925.
> The first half of this book is an important historical work, written

from the French point of view. An appendix lists French cinema patents issued from 1890 to 1900.

MAJOR GENERAL JAMES WATERHOUSE. "Notes on the early history of the camera obscura," *Photographic Journal*, Vol. XXV, No. 9. London, May 31, 1901.

GEORGES POTONNIEE. *Les Origines du Cinématographe.* Paris, 1928.

WILFRED E. L. DAY. *Illustrated Catalogue of the Will Day Historical Collection of Cinematograph and Moving Picture Equipment.* London.

SIMON HENRY GAGE AND HENRY PHELPS GAGE. *Optic Projection.* Ithaca, N. Y., 1914.
This book has a good historical bibliography.

Periodicals which contain important papers include:
Philosophical Transactions. Royal Society of London. London.
Journal. Royal Institution of Great Britain. London.
Comptes-rendus. Académie des Sciences (Institut de France). Paris.
Cosmos; revue des sciences et de leurs applications. (Also known as *Les Mondes*). Paris.
La Nature. Paris.
Scientific American. New York.
U. S. Patent Office Gazette. Washington, D. C.
Photographic Journal, including the transactions of the Royal Photographic Society of Great Britain. London.
Photographic Journal of America. Philadelphia.

CHAPTER I

ARISTOTLE. *Problems.*
On Dreams.

EUCLID. *The Elements of Geometrie* translated by H. Billingsley. London, 1570.
La Prospettiva di Euclide. Florence, 1573.

LUCRETIUS, *De Rerum Natura.*

PTOLEMY (CLAUDIUS PTOLEMAEUS). *Ptolemaei Mathematicae.* Wittenberg, 1549.
Almagest. Edited by J. Baptiste Ricciolus, S. J. 1651.

ALHAZEN. *Opticae Thesaurus Alhazeni Arabis.* Basel, 1572.

CHAPTER II

ROGER BACON. *Fr. Rogeri Bacon Opera Quaedam Hactenus Inedita.* J. S. Brewster. London, 1859.
The Opus Majus of Roger Bacon, edited with an introduction and analytical table by John Henry Bridges. Oxford, 1897-1900.

Letter concerning the marvelous power of art and of nature, and concerning the nullity of magic. Translated from the Latin by Tenney L. Davis. Easton, Pa., 1923.

Part of the Opus Tertium of Roger Bacon, including a fragment now printed for the first time, edited by A. G. Little. Aberdeen, 1912.

PIERRE MAURICE MARIE DUHEM. *Le Système du monde,* histoire des doctrines cosmologiques de Platon à Copernic. Paris, 1913-1917.

WITELO. *Vitellionis Turingopoloni Libri X.*
Basel, 1572.
Vitellionis Mathematici Doctissimi Περί 'Οπτικῆς. Nuremberg, 1535.

CHAPTER III

LEONARDO DI SER PIERO DA VINCI. *A Treatise of Painting.* Translated from the original Latin. Paris, 1651.

The Life of Leonardo da Vinci done into English from the text of the second edition of the "Lives" (by Giorgio Vasari) with a commentary by Herbert P. Horne. London, 1903.

The Literary Works of Leonardo da Vinci, compiled and edited from the original manuscripts by Jean Paul Rickter. London, 1880-1883.

Essai sur les ouvrages physico-mathématiques de Léonard de Vinci, avec des fragmens tirés de ses manuscripts apportés de l'Italie. Giovanni Battista Venturi. Paris, 1797.

GUILLAUME LIBRI. *Histoire des sciences mathématiques en Italie,* depuis la renaissance des lettres jusqu'à la fin du dix-septième siècle. Paris, 1838-1841.

GIORGIO VASARI. *Lives of Seventy of the Most Eminent Painters, Sculptors and Architects.* Edited by E. H. and E. W. Blashfield and A. A. Hopkins. New York, 1896.

FRANCESCO MAUROLICO. *Cosmographia.*
Venice, 1543.
Theoremata de Lumine, et Umbra, ad Perspectivam & Radiorum Incidentiam Facientia. Leyden, 1613.

GIROLAMO CARDANO. *De Subtilitate.*
Nuremberg, 1550.
Les Livres de Hierome Cardanus Médecin Milannois. Richard Le Blanc. Paris, 1556.

CHAPTER IV

GIOVANNI BATTISTA DELLA PORTA. *Magia Naturalis, sive de Miraculis Rerum Naturalium.* Naples, 1558. Revised and enlarged edition. Naples, 1589.
Natural Magic. London, 1657. (In this English translation the author's name is given an English form—John Baptista Porta.)

DANIELLO BARBARO. *La Pratica della Perspettiva.*
Venice, 1569.

GIOVANNI BATTISTA BENEDETTI. *Diversarum Speculationum Mathematicarum et Physicarum Liber.* Turin, 1585.

CHAPTER V

GEMMA (REINERUS) FRISIUS. *De Radio Astronomico et Geometrico Liber.*
Antwerp, 1545.

ERASMUS REINHOLD. *Theoricae Novae Planetarium.* Edited by Georgius Peurbachius. Paris, 1553.

JOHANNES KEPLER. *Ad Vitellionem Paralipomena.*
Frankfort, 1604.
Dioptrice. 1611.

FRANCOIS D'AGUILON. *Opticarum Libri Sex.*
Antwerp, 1685.

CHAPTER VI

ATHANASIUS KIRCHER. *Vita admodum reverendi P. Athanasii Kircheri, Societ. Jesu,* vir toto orbe celebratissimus. 1684.
The Latin autobiography of Athanasius Kircher, edited by Jerome Langenmantel (Hieronymus Ambrosius Langenmantelius).
Ars Magna Lucis et Umbrae. Rome, 1646. Second edition. Amsterdam, 1671.
Numerous other books by Kircher on many subjects. See Kircher's bibliography in *La Bibliothéque des Ecrivains de la Compagnie de Jésus,* by Augustin and Aloysius de Backer, and *Bibliothéque de la Compagnie de Jésus* by Charles Sommervogel.

GEORGE DE SEPIBUS VALESIUS. *Romani Collegii Societatis Jesu Musæum. Celeberrimum.* Amsterdam, 1678.
Musæum Kircherianum in Romano Soc. Jesu Collegio. Rome, 1707.

CHAPTER VII

GASPAR SCHOTT. *Magia Universalis Naturæ et Artis.*
Würzburg, 1658-1674.

CLAUDE FRANCOIS MILLIET DE CHALES. *Cursus seu Mundus Mathematicus.* Lyons, 1690.

JOHANN ZAHN. *Oculus Artificialis Teledioptricus sive Telescopium.*
Nuremberg, 1685.
Specula Physico-Mathematico-Historia Notabilium ac Mirabilium Sciendorum. Nuremberg, 1696.

CHAPTER VIII

PIETER VAN MUSSCHENBROEK. *Physicæ experimentales.*
Leyden, 1729; Venice, 1756.
   Cours de Physique Expérimentale et Mathématique. Paris, 1769.

ABBE GUYOT. *Nouvelles Recréations Physiques et Mathématiques.*
Paris, 1770.

WILLIAM HOOPER. *Rational Recreations.*
London, 1774. Second edition, 1782.

CHAPTER IX

ETIENNE GASPARD ROBERT (ROBERTSON). *Mémoires Récréatifs, Scientifiques et Anecdotiques du Physicien-Aéronaute.* Paris, 1831-33.

WILLIAM RITCHIE. "Proposal for Improving the Phantasmagoria," *Edinburgh Journal.* 1825.

CHAPTER X

JOHN AYRTON PARIS (Published anonymously) *Philosophy in Sport Made Science in Earnest.* London, 1827.

DAVID BREWSTER. *A Treatise on the Kaleidoscope.*
Edinburgh, 1819.
   The Stereoscope: Its History, Theory and the Construction, with Its Application to the Fine and Useful Arts and to Education. London, 1856.

JOSEPH PRIESTLY. *The History and Present State of Discoveries Relating to Vision, Light and Colours.* London, 1772.

CHAPTER XI

LAMBERT ADOLPHE JACQUES QUETELET, editor. *Correspondance Mathématique et Physique.* Brussels.

S. STAMPFER. *Jahrbücher* Technische Hochschule. Vol. 18, p. 237. Vienna, 1834.

E. S. SNELL. "On the Magic Disks in America," *American Journal of Science and Arts.* (Silliman's Journal). Vol. 27, p. 310. New Haven, 1835.

PETER MARK ROGET. *Animal and Vegetable Physiology,* considered with reference to natural theology. London, 1834.

   Annales de Chimie et de Physique. Paris.
   Bulletin. L'Académie Royale des Sciences, des Lettres, et des Beaux Arts. Brussels.

Annuaire. L'Académie Royale des Sciences, des Lettres, et des Beaux Arts. Brussels, 1885.

Annalen der Physik und Chemie. Edited by Johann Christian Poggendorff. Leipzig.

CHAPTER XII

FRANZ UCHATIUS. "Apparat zur Darstellung beweglicher Bilder an der Wand" (Apparatus for the Presentation of Motion Pictures upon a Wall). *Sitzungsberichte.* K. Akademie der Wissenschaften. Vienna, 1853.

KARL SPACIL. "Franz Freiherr von Uchatius," *Schweizerische Zeitschrift für Artillerie und Genie.* Vol. XLI, pp. 216-223. Frauenfeld, 1905.

CHAPTER XIII

MARCUS A. ROOT. *The Camera and the Pencil;* or the Heliographic Art, its theory and practice. Philadelphia, 1864.
Pennsylvania Arts and Sciences. A quarterly published by the Pennsylvania Arts and Sciences Society. Vol. 2, p. 25. Philadelphia, 1937.

RICHARD BUCKLEY LITCHFIELD. *Tom Wedgwood—The First Photographer.* London, 1903.

GEORGES POTONNIEE. *Histoire de la Découverte de la Photographie.* Paris, 1925.
The History of the Discovery of Photography. Translated from the French by Edward Epstean. New York, 1936.

LOUIS JACQUES MANDE DAGUERRE. *Historique et Description des Procédés du Daguerréotype et du Diorma.* Paris, 1839.

CHARLES LOUIS CHEVALIER. *Guide de Photographie.*
Paris, 1854.

VICTOR FOUQUE. *The Truth Concerning the Invention of Photography.* Nicéphore Niepce; his life, letters and works. Translated by Edward Epstean. New York: Tennant & Ward, 1935.
La Vérité sur l'invention de la Photographie. Nicéphore Niepce, sa vie, ses essais, ses travaux, d'après sa correspondance et autres documents inedita. Paris, 1867.

HENRY RENNO HEYL. "A Contribution to the History of the Art of Photographing Living Subjects in Motion and Reproducing the Natural Movements by the Lantern," *Journal.* The Franklin Institute. Vol. CXV, p. 310. Philadelphia, 1898.

CHAPTER XIV

ETIENNE JULES MAREY. *Le Mouvement.*
Paris, 1894.
Movement. London and New York, 1895.

La Méthode Graphique dans les sciences expérimentales et principalement en physiologie et en médecine. Paris, 1885.
La Chronophotographie, appliquée à l'étude des actes musculaires dans la locomotion.
The History of Chronophotography. (An extract from the *Smithsonian Report* for 1901). Washington, 1902.

EADWEARD MUYBRIDGE. *Journal.* Published by the Franklin Institute. Philadelphia, 1883.

J. D. B. STILLMAN. *The Horse in Motion,* as shown by instantaneous photography. The Muybridge photographs published under the auspices of Leland Stanford. Boston, 1882.

GEORGES POTONNIEE. *Louis Ducos du Hauron,* his life and work. Translated by Edward Epstean from the French edition of 1914. Reprinted from the *Photo-Engravers Bulletin.* February and March. New York, 1939.

CHAPTER XV

TERRY RAMSAYE. *A Million and One Nights.* New York, 1926.

ANTONIA AND WILLIAM KENNEDY LAURIE DICKSON. "Edison's Invention of the Kineto-phonograph," reprinted from the *Century Magazine,* June, 1894, with an introduction by Charles Galloway Clarke. Los Angeles, 1939.

DAYTON CLARENCE MILLER. *Anecdotal History of the Science of Sound* to the beginning of the 20th Century. New York: Macmillan, 1935.

CHAPTER XVI

MAURICE NOVERRE. *La Vérité sur l'invention de la Projection Animée.* Emile Reynaud, sa Vie, et ses Travaux. Brest, 1926.

GEORGES BRUNEL. *Les Projections Mouvementées.* Paris, 1897.

EUGENE TRUTAT. *Traité Général des Projections.* Paris, 1897.
La Photographie Animée, avec une préface de J. Marey. Paris, 1899.

GEORGES EMILE JOSEPH DEMENY. *Les Origines du Cinématographe.* Paris, 1909.

CHAPTER XVII

RAMSAYE. Lib. cit.
LUCIEN BULL. *La Cinématographie.* Paris, 1928.

Index

A

Acres, Birt, 152, 154, 176.
After-images, 18, 45.
Aguilon, François d', 46, 47, 109, 166.
Ailly, Pierre d', 26.
Alberti, Leone Battista, 30, 31, 38, 41, 65, 165.
Albertus Magnus, St., 32, 164.
Alhambra Theatre, 153.
Alhazen, 13, 21-23, 26, 31, 161, 164.
Alkindi, 164.
Almeida, 172.
American Mutoscope (& Biograph) Company, 141, 158.
Amet, Edwin Hill, 176.
Angiers, 172.
Animatograph, 153.
Anorthoscope, 94, 96.
Anschütz, Ottomar, 126, 134, 139, 143, 146, 147, 154-156, 174, 176.
Appleton, 176.
Archer, Frederick Scott, 112, 116.
Archimedes, 13, 18-22, 39, 63, 77, 103, 161, 163.
Aristotle, 13, 17, 18, 21, 22, 32, 64, 161, 163.
Armat, Thomas, 11, 154-160, 176.
Arzonis, Pierro de, 40.
Averroës, 164.
Avias & Hoffman, 176.
Avicenna, 164.

B

Babbage, Charles, 84, 169.
Bacon, Roger, 23, 24-28, 32-34, 38, 45, 68, 161, 164.
Banks, Joseph, 84.
Barbaro, Daniello, 39, 41, 166.
Barberini, Francesco Cardinal, 10, 51, 57.
Baron, Auguste, 176.
Baxter & Wray, 176.

Bayard, Hippolyte, 170.
Beale, Lionel Smith, 172, 173.
Bedts, Rider de, 176.
Benedetti, Giovanni Battista, 39-41, 166.
Bets, 176.
Bial, Albert, 11. See also Koster & Bial's Music Hall.
Bio-Phantoscope, 141.
Biograph, 158.
Bioscope:
    Demeny's, 145;
    Duboscq's, 109;
    Foucauld's, 172;
    Paul's, 176.
Bjerknes, 124.
"Black Art." See Necromancy.
Blair Company, 153.
Bliss School of Electricity, 154.
Boethius, 164.
Bouly, Léon, 150.
Bourbouze, 121, 172.
Boyle, Robert, 167.
Brahe, Tycho, 43.
Brewster, David, 83, 169, 171.
Briggs, Caspar W., 112, 114, 173.
Brown, Arthur, 120.
Brown, F., 176.
Brown, O. B., 112, 113, 172.
Brun, 176.
Burning Glasses, 19-21, 63, 65, 103, 163.

C

Cagliostro, Alessandro conte di, 76.
Calotype. See Talbot calotype process.
Camera: See also Camera lucida and Camera obscura; "battery system" (Muybridge-Isaacs), 120, 122, 126, 127, 173; motion picture, 116, 117, 125, 126, 129, 133, 136, 141, 150-153, 155, 157, 158, 174, 175, 176; portable, 45, 46, 143, 145, 146, 152, 167, 168; with microscope, 145; with projector, 142, 143.

185